The Golden Eagle

GREAT WRITERS PRAISE ANOTHER GREAT WRITER,

Robert Murphy

"A dramatic tale of high adventure . . . a splendid book, superbly written, and beautifully illustrated."

FRED GIPSON

"An absorbing book . . . about a wonderful bird."

JOHN KIERNAN

"An A-plus book . . . marvelous."

MARY ELLEN CHASE

"A delight . . . if the reader is not already an eagle fan, he will be."

ROGER TORY PETERSON

The
GOLDEN EAGLE

by Robert Murphy

Illustrated by John Schoenherr

AN AVON BOOK

AVON BOOKS
A division of
The Hearst Corporation
959 Eighth Avenue
New York, New York 10019

First Avon Printing, July, 1967

Cover illustration by John Shoenherr

Printed in the U.S.A.

For Jeannie

. . . arrogant, unwilling to give ground,
the golden eagle seems almost to disdain
the civilization that is sweeping it away.

PETER MATTHIESSEN
Wildlife in America

The Golden Eagle

Chapter 1

FROM THE ROCKY BANK of the small, swift stream at the bottom of the canyon the cliff rose up, straight as a wall, for nearly seven hundred feet into the sky. It was almost a quarter of a mile across its face, sheer and unscalable, as though a great knife had sliced a piece of the mountain away. At each side of the cliff face, framing it, the mountain rose by steep slopes and great rocky steps, by small benches where pines had taken root and clung through storms and winds and the prying fingers of winter ice. About sixty feet below the rimrock at the top, almost equidistant from the sides of the cliff, there was a shelf that thrust out over the empty air for ten feet and ran along the face for twenty. Near one end of it there was a cave four feet wide and six deep; a man on his knees could just about move around in it, and from this cave and the shelf, there was a wide and magnificent view of the canyon, across it over the lower ridge on the other side, and beyond to the far sagebrush-dotted Colorado plain that faded off into the haze to the east.

In the middle of the shelf there was a golden eagle's nest made of interlaced sticks and brush and covered on the outside with gray-green moss that blended it into the gray rock of the cliff face. It was small for an eagle's nest, being a little over three feet in diameter and not over two feet high, but this was its first year of occupancy. If the old birds survived the hazards of life, to use it again they would add to it with each succeeding year. It had been dressed around the rim with short pine branches, replaced as they dried and faded, until a week or so past; there were hind-quarters of rabbits and several ground squirrels scattered on the shelf near the nest, for the old birds had ceased to remove the remains of prey now that the young were old enough to tear up their own meat.

There were two young eagles in the nest, one much larger than the other. This was the female, and the earliest hatched; she would always be a third larger than her brother, after the manner of birds of prey. They were both well-feathered, their quills had hardened, and they were about ready to fly; the white natal down that had patched them and tipped their feathers was about gone now, and the clove brown of their plumage had a running purplish sheen. The crown and hackle feathers on the male's head were dark and would grow paler as he matured; the female's were already dark gold and gleamed in the sun. Beneath their wings, at the bases of their primaries, were white patches that would gradually darken. Their tails, except for the dark bands tipped with white at the ends, were white, black-spotted, and would gradually darken too. It would be easy to mistake them now for immature bald eagles at a distance, but their legs were feathered to the toes and the bald eagle's were not.

They had been quiet for a time, lying together in the nest, but presently the female, whom we shall call Kira, began to grow restless; she had always been the more active one. She stood, bowed her bright head, and stretched the great seven-foot wings that would soon bear her up over her back. After she folded them again, she looked at her brother, and decided to bedevil him. She often did this, and he knew he would be roughly handled; he scrambled out of the nest and ran along the ledge to the mouth of the cave. She started for him, but after several steps was distracted by the hindquarters of a jackrabbit in her path. Her foot, longer than a man's hand and armed with great, curving, needle-sharp talons, shot out and clamped upon it. She dropped it; caught and dropped it again; picked it up with her hooked beak, tossed it a foot away, and ran after it. She warmed to her work; what had started as play, mock battle, took on more serious intent, foreshadowing battles of the future that would not be playful. Her hackles rose; her foot came out again and took the hindquarters in its terrible, paralyzing grip. She looked at the prey in her foot, dropped it, flapped her wings, and screamed in triumph.

It was not a very impressive scream for a bird of her size, but golden eagles are rather silent creatures; many hawks scream more frequently and with greater volume. It is not their screaming that makes these eagles noble;

it is their great power and courage, their regal dignity, and their love of the high air that takes them far above the loftiest peaks and brings them down like dark thunderbolts upon strong prey. Their race encircles the world. In the days when falconry flourished in Europe, they were flown only by kings; Kublai Khan knew them, and the hunters of the bleak uplands of Thibet. The wild Kirghiz of the steppes caught wolves with them, and they were flown at antelope and deer in Chinese Tartary; Indians of the American West longed for their feathers to transfer to themselves in war the eagle's invincible magic.

Kira had got her mind off her brother; she moved to the ledge's lip and her dark, hooded eyes searched the canyon. Her sight was superb, fashioned to find prey at immense distances; she had many times man's accommodation and did not have to look directly at an object, for she saw in detail all over her retinas. She saw, among the scrub oak and cottonwood along the stream, where they could find a foothold among the rocks, wand lily, creeping holly grape, stonecrop, and bracted alum root blooming. She saw a rock wren, which had built its nest in a short tunnel under a stone on a slope on the canyon wall above the trees and laid a little pavement of stone chips to it, but couldn't hear its chanted song. Several least chipmunks ran in and out among the rocks. The somewhat eccentric old coyote who lived in the canyon had moved out of cover and lay drowsing in a sunny opening, muzzle on forepaws; he was so still that she didn't notice him until he awoke and snapped at a persistent fly.

She raised her head, searched the sky, and fixed her

gaze to the east; far off, a tiny dot in the blue, the old female eagle was coming in high above the other ridge. She set her wings for the long glide to the ledge, and as she came nearer Kira saw that there was prey in her foot and began to move about with anticipation. The young male had seen his mother too, and ran back from the end of the ledge. Over the canyon the old bird dropped a little, swooped up to kill her momentum, and as she landed on the ledge opened her foot and dropped a half-grown jackrabbit. As it slid toward them, both young eagles started for it; Kira's foot flashed out and she caught it. She looked at her brother and he moved back a little, remembering just in time that he was overmatched and had better wait his turn.

He watched hungrily until Kira had eaten as much as she wanted and climbed back into the nest, then moved in to finish what was left. His mother, calm and unruffled, beautiful in repose in the clear light of the Front Range, watched him with her head canted, her golden hackles bright in the sun.

The three men, carrying ropes, came out of the pines which ended a few yards back from the edge of the cliff, and it was the male eagle (called the tiercel because he is a third smaller than his mate) who saw them first. He had swung back over the ridge when he came in from the prairie; he approached from behind the men, several hundred feet over the pines, with a five-foot rattler which he had decapitated in his foot. When he saw the men directly over the eyrie, he began his alarm cry: Kiah! Kiah! Kiah! The sound echoed among the great rocks and stony spires on each side of the cliff face; a lonely trout fisherman in the stream far below heard it and looked up but could see nothing for his roof of leaves.

The tiercel swung past the edge of the precipice and circled higher, still screaming his apprehension. The old eagle on the ledge heard him, cocked her head, and saw him mounting into the sky. She knew at once that there was trouble, and jumped off the ledge. Her great wings opened and took hold on the air; she slanted off across the canyon to a place where there was usually an updraft which would help her gain altitude. She found the warm and rising current of air and began to circle higher in it; the canyon dropped beneath her, and she saw the men.

She screamed at them too, but continued to rise. Her temper was shorter than the tiercel's and the young were more her concern; had the creatures upon the top of the cliff been anything but men she would have stooped at them in fury, roaring down on folded wings to drive them away. There were few animals in her world that she wouldn't meet in battle, but her ancestors had survived the schemes and stratagems of Indian plume hunters for so many generations that it had become a racial instinct to avoid men.

They watched her as she mounted higher and drifted off to circle with the tiercel in the distance, and then dropped a rope's end over the cliff and payed out the rope until it reached the shelf. Having thus measured the length they wanted, they took the other end into the pines, ran the rope around the nearest pine—which was to be used as a snubbing post—and made the rope fast to another tree further back. They came back to the cliff's edge again, pulled up the rope, and arranged it around the lightest man so that he could sit in a loop of it and was also supported under the arms.

He walked around to assure himself that it was fast at all points, and comfortable. "I think it's all right," he said. "Suppose there are two of them?"

"Take one. We don't need them both."

"Okay."

They put a big musette bag over his shoulder, and one of them walked back to the snubbing post. The other took hold of the rope. The one who was going over the cliff turned his back on it, and holding the rope backed over the cliff's edge. It was rounded there; there was no sharp edge to fray the rope, and the man sitting in the loop, holding himself off with his feet, began his descent as the rope was slowly payed out. He looked very small and mortal against the cliff face; he glanced down once and his belly seemed to rise coldly into his throat.

The young eagles on the ledge had been puzzled by the tiercel's screaming, for they had never heard the alarm call before. They watched their mother take off, and when her voice was added to the tiercel's they began to grow uneasy. Their familiar routine had been disturbed, something was happening to which they had no key, and some of the old bird's apprehension came through to them. They both ran to the familiar nest, climbed into it, and crouched down; then Kira's eye caught movement above as the man started down the cliff face. She looked up, staring at him; the young tiercel followed her glance. Swaying a little on the end of his rope, large and alien against the sky, the man seemed all sprawling arms and legs. He was a deadly enemy, and momentarily growing nearer.

As the man descended, they moved back in the nest until they were on the inside edge of it, pressed against the rock; confusion held them there until he was almost level with them. As he came closer he grew more menacing, with his pale face looking down and the scuff of his shoes on the rock, and suddenly Kira was freed of the paralysis of fear that had held her. She jumped from the nest and ran along the shelf to the cave, and her brother followed her. They scrambled into the cave; its roof and walls closed protectively around them and shut out the sight of the invader.

The man kicked out from the cliff, and by pulling himself up a little as he swung back landed on the shelf. He had a little slack now and signaled for more by giving two jerks on the rope. They gave it to him. He could move about a little now, and although he didn't like his position and thought of being pulled up again to be dropped before the cave, he decided against this; he crawled along the shelf, pressing against the rock, to the cave. When he appeared in the mouth of it, breathing audibly and with his outlandish crawling shape outlined against the sky, the young eagles jammed their backs against the rock; their hackles rose and they stared with menace and fear.

The man grinned at them and crawled closer, spreading his arms to keep them together. It was his intention to move in a little more, crowding them, still with his arms wide, and then make a quick, sweeping grab for the legs of one of them to immobilize its feet. He could ignore the strong, hooked beak; eagles do not use their beaks for offense; but he had great respect for the damage the talons could do to him. Once they were locked in him somewhere, it would be impossible for him to get them loosened by himself; the power of an eagle's grip is unbelievable.

He crawled an inch closer, and suddenly Kira could stand it no longer. She had always been an aggressive bird, and now this trait sent her forward. Her advance was certainly more for escape than for attack, but the elements of both were in it. She ran toward the man, who was badly startled and fell back a little, jumped toward him, touched one of his extended arms, and pushed against it to launch herself through the mouth of the cave.

She had often exercised her wings on the shelf, rising and holding herself up two or three feet above it, but solid footing had always been under her and she had never dared the empty air; now she was in it. Her feet dropped and for an instant she tried to walk upon the air, but it had no substance; she was falling through it. She had a moment of terror, but then the memory of the supporting air under her wings as she exercised them and her nerves' hereditary reflexes took over. Her wings took hold on the air and her tail spread and buoyed her up; she was flying. It was a shaky and uncertain performance, straightaway and wobbling; she almost lost her flying speed and stalled several times. When rising from flat ground, eagles start slowly and heavily because of their weight; they have to exert themselves to get airborne, but Kira had the impetus of her drop and plenty of empty space under her and wasn't confronted with this condition. All she had to do was to glide at such an angle that her flying speed was maintained. This preoccupied her so much that at first she didn't realize how fast the other side of the canyon was sliding toward her. When she did

realize it, she fell into confusion, tried to turn, and came very close to stalling again. Her mother had seen her jump from the eyrie, and although her instinct told her to stay far from the men, she broke her circle, came roaring down, braked, and rose beneath Kira. Her presence and her solid back supported the young eagle and gave her confidence again, and by adroit maneuvering beautiful to see, alternately rising beneath her and dropping away, she managed to help Kira land on a wide bench on the other side of the canyon.

It wasn't a graceful landing, but at least Kira was on the ground again. She was in some disarray, but now that she had dared the air and got safely out of it for the first time she shook her feathers into place, looked around, and

bowed and talked excitedly to herself in congratulation; her mother rose away and took up her distant, watchful circling. Kira watched her go and began to run about on the bench, opening her wings and making several short, clumsy flights from one rock to another. The feeling of being airborne remained with her for a time, so enthralling that it subordinated the memory of her fright. She remembered the feel of the air, the exhilarating freedom of it, and the speed of her flight, when she was borne up, weightless, high above the earth where it was only possible to move one step at a time; perhaps she had an intimation of the keen and limitless joy of flight that would be hers in the future.

While she was preoccupied with these things, the man, with her brother hooded and crammed into the musette bag over his shoulder, emerged from the cave and was pulled up the cliff face, walking up the rock on the end of the rope. He reached the top and went over it; his companions untied the rope, coiled it up, and all of them vanished into the pines.

After they had gone Kira's mother slid down the air from her high post, screaming in relief from the tension that had held her. This unusual sound in the canyon brought an old horned owl, who lived in a pothole far below and had slept through the tiercel's alarms, blundering out to see what the screams were about. The eagle saw him; he was something to wreak her rage and frustration upon, and although they had managed to live in amity together since early in the spring she stooped and struck the owl a terrible blow. One of her rear talons opened it up like a cleaver; there was an explosion of feathers and the owl fell dead toward the stream. Before he vanished through the trees the old eagle had swung up, and landed beside Kira on the bench.

The tiercel, knowing himself safe now, came out of the sky on a long, sloping stoop with his wings half backed. He still had the rattler in his foot, and, when he landed, Kira ran to him, snatched it, and began to break into it. She was hungry again from all the excitement. Her first experience with men was over and she had got well out of it, but there would be more experiences, more encounters brought about by active ill-will, before she lived her life out.

Chapter 2

KIRA HAD BEEN CONFINED for so long to the narrow limits of the shelf, so bare and so distant from the rest of the world about her, that the clearing and the rising mountainside, studded with great boulders and dark with pines, seemed limitless and complicated. The familiar companionship of her brother was gone and the new world, into which she had come with such sudden violence, was full of shadowy vistas and mysterious movement as the afternoon wind stirred the pines. These things had been distant and now they were all around her; she had to get accustomed to them, now that the first excitement of her flight was over.

Her father, having given up his prey, flew to a dead pine nearby and perched in it; her mother launched herself in the direction of the shelf. Kira watched her land upon it, walk about, and vanish into the cave, and then sat quietly for a while looking about her. The mountainside drowsed in the afternoon sun, and the cool, dry air still held the fragrance of the pines. Just above the treetops that concealed the creek a crow, inky black, beat his leisurely way up the canyon and dropped below the treetops. Kira had seen him once before; he lived in another canyon not far off and didn't come into this one very often because the old female eagle would stoop at him when a fit of temper was on her. She often had fits of temper, for her disposition was erratic and uncertain.

She had shown this with the owl, and soon she showed it again; for the crow, coming upon the fisherman in the creek, rose above the trees again a moment before she came out of the empty cave and became a mark for her. A few feet from the cliff she saw him, ignored him at first, and then changed her mind. She rolled over and dropped on him like a thunderbolt. The crow squawked with fear, picked up his wingbeat, evaded her with a last-instant shift when she was almost upon him, and dove back into the shelter of the trees as she turned and scudded upward. Her momentum carried her up like a rocket; she hung in the sky for the space of a breath and then slid off over the western ridge.

The male eagle had watched this, turning his head to follow his mate's flight; after she was gone he shook himself and settled down into a comfortable somnolence. He was much the calmer and more even-tempered of the pair, and had already accepted the loss of one of the young birds. Kira had watched her mother too, and was excited anew.

The wild and impetuous beauty of the stoop and the recovery, the old eagle's freedom to work her will upon the air, gave her a foreshadowing of her own freedom in it and the delight that would be hers. She began to forget the strangeness of her new surroundings, and accept them. She hopped about, practiced grabbing at sticks, and presently spread her wings and tried several more flights around the clearing, beating from one great rock to another. These maneuvers were labored and clumsy because of her weight, her inexperience, and the lack of a breeze or a rising current to buoy her, but they gave her an increasing understanding of the mechanics of flight, for which she was so wonderfully fashioned. The good solid ground not far below gave her confidence and she began to pick up a little knowledge of how to use shifts of weight, balance, and power, and the feel of the air. Her inherited instinct for flight, passed down through the germ plasm of countless generations, stirred and warmed with use and aided her. These things were exciting too, and as her reflexes caught and began to learn them her pleasure increased and her sallies stretched out a little.

Her father, hunched on his pine, occasionally opened a dark eye to watch her as the afternoon waned and shadow crept up the eastern wall of the canyon. She grew tired, finally, and came to perch on the top of a great rounded rock that thrust up from the clearing. The canyon had become by now a bowl of cool blue shadow beneath the last golden line of light at the top; having used her wings at last, she looked at it with different eyes. Her mother came in from the west, landed in the pine near her mate, and talked a little. They were all together, and ready for the night.

Most pairs of golden eagles build two nests and choose one of them in which to raise their families; sometimes they use the alternate one every other year. Kira's parents had done this, building the other nest in a high dead pine further up the canyon. The old birds now wanted to use it for a while longer, not wanting to go back to the shelf again. It was on the same side as the shelf, which meant that they would have to get Kira to cross the canyon, and at first she wasn't willing to do it; she didn't want to trust herself over the great gulf of empty air. She was quite happy for the time to be making short flights from rock to rock in the vicinity of the clearing, building up her muscles with take-offs and her coordination with landings and turns, but soon her mother grew impatient with these maneuvers.

The old bird didn't like the clearing nor the pine in it, for the site was rather hemmed in; the alternate nest was higher and more in the open, and in common with most birds of prey the old eagle preferred a lofty perch with a commanding view and even when not on the lookout for prey loved to watch the play of life around her. She set about extending Kira's movements and was a rough teacher.

She kept after Kira; she jostled her and crowded her toward the empty air, but she was always ready to lend her back, rising beneath Kira as she had done on the first day. She cut down on Kira's food and somehow indicated to her mate that he should do the same thing to make Kira fly out to her when she came in with prey in her foot. At these times she would take perch on a rock across the canyon, a deliberate provocation. After she got Kira to cross to her she went a step further, flying to and fro out of reach with a ground squirrel.

When Kira could stand it no longer she flew out. The old eagle allowed her to come almost close enough to snatch the squirrel, then sideslipped away; Kira overshot her. Her mother rose past her in a tight spiral, and avoided her again. Kira chased her, flying better than she knew because her mind was on the squirrel rather than on her flying; the old eagle carried on her game, always out of reach, occasionally yelling at her. Kira screamed back in frustration and the canyon resounded with their thin clamor; presently the old eagle bounded higher, hovered an instant, and dropped her prey. It fell, turning slowly in the air; Kira swung a tight turn, too late to catch it. She had to stoop after it, and did so instinctively rather than on purpose. She

was into her stoop before she realized it, folding her wings
and dropping head down like a stone.

The air through which she plunged sharpened its tone;
the floor of the canyon slid up, and Kira screamed at the
fierce exhilaration of it; she plummeted toward the squirrel
and reached it, her foot snatched it. Her tail spread and bit
into the air and brought her curving up; with wings half-
opened she scudded upward until her momentum was gone,
and then came down on a rock close to the pine where her
father sat watching.

It had not been a very long stoop but it had been her first
one—a discovery; the memory of it ran like fire along her
nerves. She hopped about on the rock until her excitement
abated, and then tore up the squirrel and ate it. When she
was finished she jumped off the rock and flew out over the
canyon again.

She hadn't soared before, but this time she found a warm
and rising air current and circled within it to be buoyed up.
Men in their gliders, in powerless flight, have nerves that
are still too earthbound to tell them whether they are rising
in an ascending current or losing altitude in their normal
glide path; they must have an instrument called a variome-
ter to tell them this, but Kira didn't need an instrument.
She came of a soaring race, and the knowledge was part of
her heritage. This was her first time to soar and she blun-
dered a little; she went beyond the invisible boundary of
the rising air several times, but her mother, who had risen
with her, stayed within it, and by guiding on her Kira found
the updraft again.

The floor of the canyon dropped away, and the crests on

either side. The vast and lonely country opened up: the pine-covered ridges and the plateau, the dark, hard, broken line of mountains far beyond it to the west, the wandering and precipitous canyons of the Front Range, the Spanish Peaks to the south—those two great ancient volcanoes around which Indian legends gathered and by which pioneers had found their way, called by the early Spanish explorers The Breasts Of The World, and the weathered lava dikes that radiated out from them on the plain. The rolling sagebrush-dotted foothills and the flat prairie stretched away to be lost in haze to the east, and the distant city of Pueblo sent the smoke of its steel mills into the sky. The great land, with its sweeping distances and cloud shadows, its great areas of dark pines and bare, gray peaks, would soon be hers to wander about in and to know before maturity came to her and she found a tiercel to mate with her and an eyrie that would end her wandering. The longing, vague and unde-fined as yet, to fly off and be lost and free in it half awoke in her for the first time.

Now that Kira was in the air and had confidence in herself, the old eagles took up their headquarters in the alternate nest in the pine. They were happier when their lives were centered around a place that held a happy association with their courtship and their splendid, reckless mating flights early in the year. The territory had been a compromise at first. The tiercel, ten years older than Kira's mother, had lost his previous mate toward the end of the difficult winter when, famished and unable to find prey, she had fed on a calf carcass poisoned for coyotes. He had wanted to nest on the rise of the Front Range overlooking the prairies where he liked to hunt. Kira's mother, coming to maturity, had wanted to get back into the peaks; she was more suspicious than the tiercel and wanted the wildest possible country for her first eyrie. The loss of one of her young had proved her right; and although she had accepted the vicinity rather grudgingly, if anything untoward happened in it her uncertain temper was upset. Despite this she was a good mother and spent much of her time with Kira, showing off tricks of flight for Kira's emulation and forcing her to her utmost by mock attacks. She didn't like the prairie and was reluctant to hunt there; occasionally the tiercel would go off by himself to the foothills for a few hours, but usually they were all together and Kira could watch them both.

Young eagles stay longer with their parents than other raptorial birds; living longer and developing more slowly, they need a lot of flying to bring them to their best, and their size and weight impose special difficulties that smaller raptors don't have to cope with. Much of Kira's life would be spent in soaring, in knowing and utilizing the great ocean of air and its shifts and currents and its dangers, as violent and destructive as the wild moods of the sea. Eagles avoid expending their energy in direct flights from place to place; they prefer to gain an elevation sufficient to enable them to glide or soar to their destinations, and to do this Kira would have to learn from her parents the moods of the air and how to find thermals and stay within them or use winds deflected from rough or rising ground. It was easier to learn these things from her mother and father than to work them out for herself.

She delighted in flying and couldn't get enough of it; she was slower in learning to hunt. Young birds of prey are not born with the desire to kill for themselves; it comes to them in its season. One day they do not have it, and the next they are changed; one day they will sit companionably next to another living creature and the next the armored foot will flash out. It was one of Kira's idiosyncrasies that she was slow in her killing.

She would sail about with the old birds and watch them at their hunting, then join them on the ground and beg to be fed. The tiercel accepted this with his usual good nature, but his mate began to grow impatient; she had spent a long time feeding nestlings and her temper was beginning to fray. Several times she stared threateningly at the tiercel and moved a step or two toward him when he tried to share his prey with Kira, and presently he gave up and began to go off more by himself; Kira's mother missed him and her temper grew shorter still.

Finally, after she had caught a rabbit and Kira's importunities grew too much for her, she jumped into the air, swung a circle, and bearing down on Kira gave her a buffet that rolled her over and over. This took the tension out of her for the time and apparently she was sorry for it, for she returned quietly, shared the rabbit with Kira, and took her to bathe further down the canyon where it widened out into an old beaver meadow and the stream flattened out.

Kira was wary of her at first, but she hadn't bathed before and the procedure, as well as the novelty of the surroundings, interested her so much that she soon forgot her chastisement. Wild iris, wild rose, and candytuft were still blooming in the checkered light among the elder and willow bushes; the old bird, ducking her head under, ruffling her feathers and rolling about, scattered the glittering water drops. For a time Kira watched her and then, stepping gingerly into the cold, clear water, tasted it and soon was emulating her mother. It was a new pleasure; before she was through she was very wet. Stepping out on to the stream's edge they spread their wing and tail feathers, drying them in the sun and dressing them by pulling them one by one through their beaks, pausing to watch mayflies hatching and trout slashing at them or a dipper, a water ouzel, flitting about, giving snatches of its lovely song, vanishing beneath the surface to run about on the bottom to catch insects and pop out of the stream again.

Kira felt wonderfully clean and exhilarated as she dried; she wanted to stay longer and watch the creatures of the stream and the stream itself as it slid with shifting, broken patterns around the rocks, but her mother had other ideas. She walked through the streamside thicket and took to the air, and Kira followed her. She flew still further down the canyon, and rose partway up its side to land on the top of a great broad rock. There were scattered pines on the slope below it, and patches of scrub oak; further down, the slope flattened out and there were fewer trees. There was a colony of ground squirrels there, for the place suited them and was open enough for the sunshine, which they liked, to penetrate.

Although the old eagle usually hunted from the air, she had found this place to her liking; she could jump off the rock and glide down the slope at speed to pick up a squirrel on the flat. She walked to the edge of the rock to watch below, and Kira joined her. A pair of Steller's jays and their two young scolded at them for a few minutes, grew tired of it, and flew off. Quiet fell, and the shadows slowly lengthened; far down the slope a porcupine backed clumsily down a pine and moved slowly and erratically across the slope until a curve of the ground hid him. A white-winged junco in a pine nearby sang its twittering song as it moved busily about, flew toward the rock, saw the two eagles, and hastily ducked back into the pine again with a flash of its white belly and outer tail feathers.

The ground squirrels, which had seen the eagles come down the canyon and had gone underground, having grown very cautious because of the old eagle's several forays, began at length to reappear in the entrances of their burrows. They took long and careful looks around before deciding to emerge and run the gauntlet of the danger that lately seemed to be hanging forever over them. Unseen by the eagles on the rock, a shrew went around its base and under a fallen tree beside it; it was scarcely two and a half inches in length and weighed one-fifth of an ounce, but it ate three times its weight in a day. Its ravening appetite drove it to a series of desperate and frantic battles with grubs, insects, and even mice, and gave it no rest; it had no time to watch for predators.

The boldest of the squirrels, having decided that nothing threatened him, came out and began to forage. Kira watched him with interest, for several of his cousins had made meals for her; the old eagle stretched her neck toward him a little and tightened her feathers. He moved further from his burrow and a tree concealed him; the old eagle jumped from the rock. She dropped close to the ground, opened her wings, and slid down the slope toward him. Her speed increased; she shortened sail and rolled from one side to the other, sliding around the trees in her path; the rapidity of her maneuvers seemed almost incredible for a bird of her size.

e shifted her course, flashed around the last tree that
oncealed him, and picked him off the ground before he
new she was anywhere in the vicinity, scudded up through
n opening in the pines, and vanished. Kira had a momen-
ry glimpse of her with the squirrel in her foot as she went
rough an opening and began to shuffle about with antici-
ation, but the old eagle didn't return; she had gone off to
de and eat the squirrel herself.

Kira waited with increasing impatience, and finally took
f to look for her. She rose above the pines and flew up and
own the canyon, but she couldn't find her mother. She had
aited too long, in any case; the sun had dropped so low
at even the pines on the summit of the ridge were in
adow now and there was no reflected light in the canyon.
arkness was rising like a tide from below, outlines were
ding into it, and everything was growing dim; it was time
r the owls to be out. The cooling air buoyed Kira no
nger, and she turned heavily for the nest in the pine; by
e time she had reached it there was just enough light for
er to perch. The tiercel was there and spoke to her, but
e other eagle had not returned. A fox working the edge
f the stream below squalled once and fell silent; stars began
o appear, and Kira fluffed up her feathers and prepared to
eep.

he rattle of the tiercel's feathers as he shook himself awoke
er. The sky to the east was paling rosily in the dawn, and
he was hungry. She complained a little, a low, whining
ote, and stretched first one leg and wing together and then
e other—a gesture that falconers, who have ancient terms
r many of a bird's actions, call "mantling." Her mother

was still nowhere in sight and the tiercel, after yawning and looking all about, launched himself, drifted out over the canyon, and turned to rise over the eastern ridge.

Kira watched him for a moment, and then feeling left alone dropped from the pine and flew after him. He continued to rise, circling up, and was soon above the ridge. As Kira came above and passed it, the long rugged line of the Front Range, broken by buttresses, stretched out as far as she could see on each side of her, commanded to the south by the bulk of the Spanish Peaks, descending on its eastern face to the foothills and the plain. She had never been this way before because her mother avoided the plain; she had only glimpsed it from her highest pitch above the canyon, and the flat expanse seemed to have no boundary or limit except the far distant haze. The sun cleared the horizon and the prairie was washed with unbroken golden light, flat and open to the sky, endless, with thin, infrequent and wandering lines of trees beyond the rolling foothills that subsided like waves upon the beach of the plain.

Fifty miles or so to the east of her, on the Arkansas River, there had once been several posts for the fur trade—the Pueblo, now a city, run for a while by the mulatto mountain man Jim Beckwourth, that great liar, and Bent's Fort. In a land where Indians were debauched with whisky and cheated wherever possible the Bents and their partner St. Vrain had treated the Cheyennes and Arapahoes with unheard-of fairness, maintained a sort of prairie truce, and prospered. They grew richer after the beaver were trapped out as suppliers to emigrant wagon trains and carriers in the Santa Fe trade, as a station on the Oregon Trail. Kit Carson knew the place, and John Charles Frémont and

Francis Parkman; probably the earlier Spaniards from the south, before it was thought of, had moved about near it sweating in their armor and seeking cities of gold.

There had been no golden cities; the great herds of buffalo were gone, and most of the prairies had been settled and broken by the plow or overgrazed. The native grasses that had held the soil had been ruined and the land foolishly prepared for the eroding fingers of the wind; but here, in a great and lonely triangle, the short grass had been let alone. Antelope still grazed in it, there were a few large ranches and not many roads, and the tiercel liked it for his hunting. He had been hatched in an eyrie high above it; he made his descents in a series of steps, checking his drop occasionally to search the ground for prey.

Kira drew in closer to him as he made these momentary checks. There were several magpies flying about, long-tailed birds showy in their black and white plumage, seemingly easy targets in their casual flight, but the tiercel paid no attention to them; he had long since learned that they were clever and shifty and not worth the effort to pursue. He went on, and presently a black-tailed jackrabbit, disturbed by a hunting rattlesnake, jumped up and bounded across the grass.

The tiercel swung and went into a long, slanting stoop at it, and Kira stooped after him; it was a reflex action with her. She was heavier than he and her speed was greater, but she couldn't catch up with him. The rabbit saw them both. He took a spy-hop, higher than the rest, and saw a thick, high old post standing not far off; before the tiercel reached him he got to it and crouched close beside it. The tiercel couldn't get at him there, and swung up; Kira checked her stoop above him. There was a sudden new excitement in her, a hot stirring of the blood, that her mother had not been able to awaken; the rabbit bounding across the open grass and the stoop had awakened it. She swung and hovered, staring at the crouching creature pressed against the post.

She expected the tiercel to give up and leave it, but he didn't; he was going to play the game he had often played with his mate. He dropped to the ground near the post and ran toward it. The rabbit leaped out, and Kira dropped after it. She had sufficient height for the speed she needed; she swept down and closed the rabbit, and as he tried to dodge away her great foot flashed out and caught him. It was a strong rabbit, a little over half her weight; it bucked and jumped desperately and swung her about, but her other foot closed on its head and finished it. She came to ground and stood on it in triumph, with her aquiline head high and her hackles up. It was a stirring moment for her. She had crossed the dividing line and was a dependent no longer, but a hunter, an aristocrat of the air whose hard discipline calls for the utmost from the nerves, the sinews, and the brain, not for the practice of cruelty but in order to live.

Golden eagles hunt together, as she and her father had done, and share their prey; this time she wanted it for herself. She looked around to see the tiercel and warn him away, but he understood her feeling. He landed on top of the post and gave no sign of leaving it; he would wait until she had finished. If she left anything he would eat it, and then they would fly together again.

While Kira broke into the rabbit her father looked about, watching a distant flight of horned larks as they rose and fell at their feeding, stringing out over the prairie. Beyond them, where there was a little-used road, a car moved along before a plume of dust and stopped. The tiercel turned his attention to it, for he had never seen a car so close before. His eye caught a movement within it, and then a bright wink as the telescopic sight swung across the path of the morning sunlight. These things disturbed him and he had half-opened his wings to fly when the bullet smashed into him, knocking feathers out of his back and throwing him down to sprawl loosely on the ground.

Being lower than the tiercel and shielded by a little rise of the ground, Kira hadn't seen the car. The *whop* of the bullet and its banshee screech, the explosion of feathers and the tiercel's sprawling fall startled her into jumping off the ground. She saw the man getting out of his car and knew him for one of the long-legged enemies who had raided the eyrie; she was sufficiently familiar with the attitudes of death to know that the tiercel would never get up again. She knew that she must flee the place, and quickly. Her wings took hold on the air and she swung for the canyon that would give her sanctuary, rising as she went.

Chapter 3

LONELY AND ILL AT EASE, Kira sat hunched in the pine above the nest until early afternoon, when her mother came in. The old eagle had a hen mallard in her foot; she had seen a family of them resting in a pool from afar, approached cannily, whipped around a pine, and picked it out of the flock as they jumped, startled, into the air. She seemed to sense from Kira's bearing that her daughter had killed for herself, and could now go her own way. The bond between her and her surviving nestling, which had been so strong for a time, had almost come to an end; the tiercel's disappearance would hasten the ending. She had missed the tiercel and had been looking for him; she was restless and preoccupied.

Kira was so glad to see her that she did a foolish thing;

she jumped into the air, flew toward her mother, and rolling sideways tried to snatch the mallard from her foot.

This maneuver, so playful in intent, suddenly brought the uneasy older bird to the last of her short patience. She rose above Kira, swung a tight half circle, and screaming with rage stooped at Kira with the intention of killing her. Kira was confused by this sudden attack, and frightened. She reacted instinctively; she rolled over, closed her wings, and dropped belly up toward the floor of the canyon to avoid the coming stroke. The old eagle, expecting her to rise, was thrown out a little by this unexpected shift. She flashed past, her foot out, and her lethal rear talon which would have sliced through Kira's ribs missed by a fraction of an inch. Had she swung back she would have had Kira at her mercy, for Kira was in too much disarray to recover quickly, but the mood to kill changed as swiftly as it had come upon her. She plunged down into the canyon, checked momentarily, and vanished into the trees along the stream.

Kira was so intent upon collecting herself and avoiding the stroke that she didn't see her mother go. Although her maneuver had saved her life, it had put her at an immense disadvantage, for the other bird had control of the air and even now should be swinging back; to right herself would take too much time when every instant counted against her. She was hurried, confused by her mother's sudden turning against her, and desperate, but in her extremity instinct came to her aid again; it told her to get out of the air. She rolled a little more, got her head down, and plunged for the earth. The air roared past her; she checked her fall as late as she dared, and dropped into an opening between two great rocks.

Holly grape covered most of the ground in the opening and she sat among its prickly leaves and young berries until her heart returned to its normal beat; then she shook her feathers into place and moved out on to the open slope. She searched the sky and couldn't find her mother hanging in it, waiting for her, but that threat didn't concern her now. The experience was over and she had survived it; it had changed her a little more. Whatever softness had remained in her was gone; deep within her she was somehow aware that her instinctive reactions (which in a bird take the place of thought) were swift and trustworthy and could be relied upon.

In effect, she had moved a long step toward confidence in herself, and was free of the eyrie and the canyon at last. There was no longer anything that she needed in it; memories of her mother's attack upon her and the tiercel's death hung over it, and the man crouching in the cave, and her nestmate that she would never see again. She had had enough of it. She jumped into the air and swung up the canyon, to rise on the sun-warmed air and follow the canyon's turnings toward the higher country to the west.

The earth had not begun to cool, yet; the great bubbles of warm and rising air, as she found and circled in them, buoyed her higher and higher into the sky. She reached the point of her furthest wandering from the eyrie and went on in her new freedom. As she mounted into the cooler and thinner air the great rocky backbone of the continent opened up. Once more she saw the Spanish Peaks massive to the south, the distant snow-patched loom of the Sangre de Cristo to the west, the far dark bulk of Pikes Peak northward, and all the tumbled sea of summits and valleys in between. The floor of the canyon rose steadily beneath her; the white gleam of little clumps of aspen began to appear in it as the country marched higher. The sky had been clear when she left but clouds had moved into it and now covered the declining sun. A storm was coming and she met the first gust of wind preceding it and then a stouter turbulence;

lightning slashed the rolling clouds and Kira dropped into the canyon to find a sheltered corner in the lee of a rocky outcrop to wait out the storm. It began to rain. Thunder rolled about Kira, echoing among the rocks, and lightning stabbed the gloom; the runoff down the slope muddied the stream.

In half an hour the storm was over and the sun came

out again, lower now, sending long, slanting golden shafts into the canyon, glittering on pendant raindrops, and giving Kira's surroundings a fresh and newly washed look in the cooler air. She was growing hungry again; the bullet that had finished the tiercel had interrupted her morning meal, and night was coming on. She wanted to feed before dark; she sat for a while drying her feathers and looking for quarry, but nothing moved within her view and after a time she took up her way again. She had to fly now for there were no updrafts to buoy her, and at the edge of dusk she came to the canyon's end. It widened into a great semicircular meadow sloping up to the plateau, with a pond in it that an old beaver, working alone, had made by damming the stream near the spring that was its source. There were a few trout in it, dimpling the surface in their evening rise, but they would soon be back in the stream again; the old beaver had died three weeks before and his dam was already falling into disrepair. A few heavy storms would wash it out. Life had concentrated there for a little; heart-leaved buttercup, wood beauty and Frémont's geranium had bloomed around it, and tansy aster and goldenrod; the willows and alders had found its silted marshy edges to their liking and grew thick, and it had been lively with birds.

Kira almost perched for the night in a big dead ponderosa pine near the dam, but changed her mind and flew past it. She was quite hungry now, but wanted to leave the canyon. She kept on in the failing light, up the long slope to the tableland beyond. It was a grassy, parklike place and spacious, with Indian paintbrush and scattered pines growing in the pebbly soil. A young rabbit, deciding that the twilight world was safe to move about in, jumped up in front of her and she went after it. Its white, bobbing tail was her mark in the twilight and she caught it too far back and had a struggle with it; she ended its life, and not liking the gathering darkness on the ground took it up on to the top of a weathered rock and ate it. The stars were bright when she finished it, and after cleaning her beak on the stone she settled down for the night.

Dawn, calm and still and golden, reclaimed the world from the creatures of the night and found Kira still on her rock; she shook herself and watched the sun break free and take the sky. She was in no hurry to move, having fed well at dusk. She couldn't soar until the earth warmed and the rising currents would buoy her, and she wouldn't hunt again until the bits of fur she had swallowed with her meat were rolled up in a firm cocoonlike shape and brought up as a casting from her crop.

The morning wore quietly on, and toward the middle of it Kira cast and then grew restless. She wasn't hungry; that would come later; it was a desire to move about, to see what the world about her held, that got her off the rock. She didn't fly very high; presently she came out of the scattered pines to a treeless, rolling country, a great area of grass that was beginning to brown. There was a white ranch house in the middle of it, with its weathered barns, pole corrals, and scattered whiteface cattle, very lonely in its isolation; she swerved in her course to come closer to the buildings, for she was curious about them. The rancher's two German shepherds saw her wide, flat wings against the sky, looked at one another, and ran out after her. She swung and a belated discretion took hold of them; they ran back to the barns and were lost to sight. A man came out of one of the barns and shaded his eyes with his hand to look at her, and seeing him she swung again and went on.

The land continued to rise before her to a horizon where the tableland forest took over from the grass, a dark, sweeping, serrated line against a wide sky with a distant reef of clouds. There were spruce and fir in it now, and aspen; it was close growing, clean on the ground but too thick for hunting, and she rose higher. Far off and all around, the world rose to tree-covered ranges patched with cloud shadows, and peaks that turned bare and gray as the forests on their sides fell away at timberline. Her little rise in altitude had opened up the world so much that in the clear air her view seemed limitless, spacious enough for a lifetime of wandering.

The distant peaks, massive and mysterious, attracted her as a magnet attracts a compass needle and she gained a little more height; but when the land to the south began to fall away toward a stream valley she swung toward it, circled several times, and began her descent. She made it slowly, as though undecided, but there was no real question; the attraction of the peaks was very strong, but she needed a little more time before trying that high, keen air and the lonely, ancient silence. The walls of the canyon that had been her home, although they had lost their long hold upon her, still held a shadowy power over her recollection and brought her down.

She dropped toward a wide and pleasant meadow between the pine-covered ridges where grass and sage, willows and pale-trunked aspen grew and the stream meandered over its scattered stones. Long ago it had been a large beaver pond but in the early eighties, in the wasteful scramble for pelts that marked the mountain fur trade toward its end, two free trappers from down Taos way had breached the dam and clubbed all the beaver before a party of Utes had surprised and killed them both. The Utes had usually fought the Plains Indians and been friendly toward the whites, but their hearts had been bad at the moment; they looked upon the beaver as a resource to be husbanded, and were enraged by such wanton destruction. The trappers' bones had long since moldered away in the accumulated silt of the pond's bottom, and the place had become a beaver meadow bright with flowers in their season.

It was a lonely, quiet place, so difficult to reach and far from any road that few fishermen ever got into it. As Kira circled down she saw a fox hunting mice, dropping upon them with its forepaws; she stooped at it, but it eluded her and vanished into the underbrush. She found a little backwater in the stream at the tail of a riffle; a big cutthroat trout arrowed out of it, and she watched it go and stepped into the riffle and bathed in the cold, clear water. Very wet, she hopped upon a streamside rock, spread her wings and tail, and let the sun and her body heat dry her; she pulled her primaries and tail feathers through her beak to dress them, and took a long time preening herself and watched a water ouzel about its affairs.

She liked the little valley; for a half mile on either side of her it was fairly level, the grass grew high in it, and the crests of the surrounding hills were low and far enough away so that she didn't feel hemmed in by them. The place was sufficiently higher than the home canyon she had left for little hints of autumn; the aspen leaves showed a brighter silver when the wind turned them up, and the violet-green swallows that had raised their broods in treeholes were growing restless to be gone on their migration to Mexico.

Washed clean and not hungry yet, Kira was in no hurry to be on the wing; she was content to sit in the cool sunshine and watch the life about her. It took its own time to reveal itself throughout the long afternoon. Several Western bluebirds, like lively little pieces of the sky, moved about her, and the water ouzel flitted up and down the stream singing its pretty song; a doe and her fawn came to the stream to drink several hundred yards below her, graceful, hesitant, and cautious in the sunshine, looking about with their ears cocked. They disturbed a lonely yellow-breasted chat in a streamside tangle, which hopped about them protesting mildly for a while and flew off. Presently the trout returned to its riffle, lay in the line of the current, and for a time slashed at hatching mayflies. Later a pileated warbler, already dropping down toward lower country, made a scurry in the underbrush nearby but Kira never saw it; later still three nighthawks came down the stream, catching insects in their erratic flight, the white spots showing on their narrow, rakish wings. They kept up a running nasal communication with each other, and Kira watched their zigzag flight with interest until they were out of sight.

A screaming flicker, closely pursued by a big female Cooper's hawk, fled past within a few feet of Kira; the hawk caught it not far off and came down, and after staring at Kira for a long moment bore it off down the stream. The light of the descending sun left the tops of the pine-covered ridges around her, and shadow crept down the wild slopes; Kira's view drew in with the gathering darkness. Above

western ridge, behind the turn of the stream, the sky
wly turned a pale, clear green. Kira left her rock and
w to a high, lightning-killed pine to roost before the sky
led to darkness and stars. Far off a horned owl jarred the
with its ventriloquial hooting, and Kira settled down for
night.

broad-tailed hummingbird, his gorget gleaming like crim-
mail in a ray of early sunshine, found Kira still on her
ch and paused to object to her. He swung in front of her,
vering, fixed her with a beady eye, and squeaked disap-
oval. No longer than one of her toes, tiny and indomitable,
flitted about first on one side and then on the other,
wings trilling, and finally went off when she raised her
lden crest at him. He had wasted enough time on her,
the blossoms he lived upon were growing harder to find;
would soon embark on his long trip to the south.

Sunlight crept up the ridges, and the early mist above
stream thinned and disappeared; presently a kingfisher
w rattling up the stream and Kira, having sat long enough,
t into the air. A breeze was coming down the valley, and
ra used it to gain a few hundred feet of altitude. She
lowed the valley as it wound its way between the ridges,
t very high; there was occasional white water under her,
ew families of mallards in the pools, and sometimes a
le spotted sandpiper or two running about and tipping up
the bars.

After a few miles a road turned into the valley and ran
ng the stream; the valley narrowed, and finally Kira came
the beginning of a canyon. The walls closed in, and on
narrow flat between their precipitous and rocky walls a

thick growth of aspen appeared, close-growing, encouraging a growth of shade-loving plants that gave the place an oddly tropical air. Several cars moved along the road as it twisted to follow the stream that was all falls and rapids now, and Kira mounted higher. Presently she came out into a great bowl with a lake in the middle of it, the source of the stream, surrounded with reeds and alders, running off into marsh and beaver dams along the main feeder stream to the west and then to aspens again as the land rolled higher. To the south the rise was gradual, dotted with sage and occasional trees, but in front of Kira and to the north the mountain rose like a wall, craggy and steep, until the pines clinging to it thinned out and gave way to bleak gray rock and sky patched with a few high cumulus clouds. It was the first time she had been close to timberline.

There were several boats on the lake, with fishermen in them; a few camping trailers and tents stood among the aspens beyond the lake, and the smoke that rose from their cooking fires was caught and dispelled by the flawed breeze from the peak. Seeing the men, Kira swung south over the rising hills and found an updraft, circling in it until the men were small and harmless, crawling over the rippled water in their boats or moving among the pale aspen trunks. She didn't like their proximity but the place held her; she didn't want to leave it yet. There were a few more cumulus clouds now and she circled higher in the thermal currents that fed them, carried up in the cool silence until she was lost to the fishermen's sight.

She mounted higher into the cold and thinning air, and higher still; the peak sank beneath her. Behind it, across the great shoulders of the mountain, the high tundra rolled under her, treeless, stony, a dun-colored world so inhospitable that nothing grew over three or four inches high. Dwarf willow, vaccinium, alpine columbine, stonecrop, and arctic gentian hugged the thin soil, all perennials because their summer was too short to bloom and form their seeds in one season. There was lichen on the rocks and mosses between them; rosy finches and pipits liked this world of miniature flowers and trees that hugged the earth and had hurried into bloom at the edge of winter's receding snow and endured the bitter whip of the wind. Their short, bright summer was nearly over, and snow would presently cover them again.

Hunger began to awake in Kira but her pitch, so high above the world, was such a delight that she didn't heed it for a time. Finally an overcast moving into the west, dark and shifting and shot with coppery light, brought her down enough to scan the tundra. A storm was coming, and she wanted to feed before it caught her at the edge of night and enforced hunger on her until the morrow. At first she saw nothing in all the dun-colored expanse, and then far off a marmot moved out from its burrow. It was also of a mind to feed well before the storm sent it into its dark hole in the stony earth, and forgot some of its habitual caution. Kira made a long, slanting stoop at it, her big, dark shape cleaving the roaring air. It turned as she checked momentarily above it, hearing her, and leaped for its burrow; she flipped over and dropped with her feet out, but missed it. She landed, disgruntled, and sat looking about for a few minutes but saw nothing except a few pipits flying restlessly about in the distance before the coming storm.

Kira opened her wings as the first wailing gust reached

her and was snatched off the ground. A few snowflakes hissed past her and the wind, rough and peremptory, tried to tumble her about. She wheeled and for a little gave herself to it, scudding over the tundra, and then turned into it again and crabbed across it until she was in the lee of the peak. The lake had turned leaden beneath the darkening sky and whitecaps crawled over it; the aspen leaves showed a dancing silver in the wind. There was thunder in the distance and as Kira dropped down the face of the peak, rocking and yawing in the shifting push of the wind, the peak faded into the overcast which descended like a veil and soaked up the light. The slanting, wind-harried rain began and turned to hail, and to get out of it and the wind Kira dropped fast for the little valley of the stream that fed the lake.

She came down through a break in the aspens, where a small beaver pond had opened up their canopy, landed near the dam, and ran a few yards to get into the lee of a great rock. Now that she was down the storm suddenly increased in fury; Kira had never seen its like. Lightning was almost continuous, and crashing thunder rocked the earth; roaring wind tore at the aspens and they bowed low under its weight, shedding twigs and leaves that whirled off into the blinding rain and hail. Muddy water poured down the slope around Kira, gullying the gravelly soil and washing over her feet; she wanted to move but could see no better place to go in the riotous gloom. The war drums of the thunder rolled to a crescendo and a bolt of lightning struck a tall dead pine nearby, splitting it like a fiery ax and showering limbs about. Kira jumped at the shock of it and opened her wings; a heavy piece of a limb hit her right one a hard and glancing blow, bounced off the rock near her head, and rolled down the slope.

After the stab of pain the wing went numb and she had no control over it; it hung down beside her and she could neither fold it nor get it up. It was not broken, but it was so severely injured that it wouldn't function, and its lack would bind her to the earth.

Chapter 4

THE STORM MOVED ON after the sun had set, leaving the sodden ground covered with leaves and torn branches and the grove full of cold mist; presently the quarter moon cleared the eastern ridge and lit it with a diffused and spectral glow. Kira was very wet, and at first didn't understand what had happened to her. To use her wings had been no more a matter of volition than to breathe; they moved and carried her aloft and balanced her when she needed them on the ground, folded out of the way when they weren't needed, automatically taking care of themselves and of her. The injured one tried many times to raise itself and fold, and each time was stopped by a stab of pain; then she tried consciously to raise and fold it, and was stopped again.

Finally she was brought to realize that it had best be let alone, and she had to accept that.

She shivered in the clammy mist until her body heat dried her, but didn't sleep. She didn't like to be on the ground, where any enemy could get at her, and would have moved as far as she was able if she could have seen anything in the darkness and the mist. For a time the grove was quiet except for the trickle and murmur of run-off water, but later the two beavers in the little pond came ashore and started to cut down an aspen thirty or forty yards away. She could hear their teeth at work and didn't know what the sounds meant, and so kept watch through the long night.

The hours of complete darkness after the moon set behind the peak finally passed and the pale glow of dawn lightened the misty grove; the beavers left their half-cut tree and went back to their pond again. It grew quiet in the grove, but Kira's view was still limited. She wanted to get out of the thick-growing aspens into the open where she could get into the air when the mist cleared. She remembered seeing the big rising meadow dotted with sagebrush on the other side of the dam, and started toward it. The first primary of her right wing dragged on the ground, and the wing caught in the underbrush; it was a troublesome thing. She crossed the muddy top of the dam and worked her way through the brush on the other side until she was in the clear. The mist was thinning now and the visibility was better; she could see for a few yards around her, and jumped into the air.

Her good wing took its stroke but her injured one did not, and stabbed her with pain besides; she fell heavily and sprawled on the ground. The indignity filled her with rage;

she bounded up with her crest erect and whirled about ready to strike, but there was nothing to strike. She tried again and fell once more, and then stood panting with pain and shock as the realization of her condition became clear.

She stood for a long time as the mist slowly lifted, immobile and withdrawn as she made the ultimate adjustment, and then stared with longing at the clearing sky.

Not much later three teen-agers from one of the camps near the lake went up the faint trail that passed on the other side of the beaver pond, talking and laughing together, and Kira followed their voices until they were out of hearing. They had their lunches with them and intended to climb to the tundra, for one of them wanted some Kodachromes of the fragile flowers there, and their passing, so close to where Kira stood in the open, made her realize how exposed she was and how necessary it was for her to get into cover.

When she was sure the three were gone she returned the way she had come, crossing the dam and the trail again but making a wide detour around the rock where the limb had struck her. The location of the camps was clear in her mind, and she moved away from them. Her halting course took her up the slope in the direction of the steep rise of the mountain and the peak; perhaps if the campers hadn't been below she would have gone in that direction anyhow, for to be high was her desire and she would do what she could to satisfy it.

The aspens gradually thinned and gave way to pines and sage, and the ground grew rockier. At first her wing hampered her badly in this sort of going. It caught on things, and although she had strong legs and was fast-moving and active on the ground she had always used her wings for balance, and now that balance was gone; she had to learn to balance with one wing. She worked her way upward until the slope grew too precipitous and the rocks too large and difficult, found a great boulder that she could manage, and scrambled to the top of it; from it she could see most of the bowl below. A pair of prairie falcons, wandering about the high country now that they had raised their young and got them off on their own, dropped down to bedevil her. They knew that she was helpless; they ripped the air above her bright head in a series of stoops, finally wearied of their sport, and went away.

At first Kira wasn't greatly concerned with hunger, for there was a good deal of residual fat on her. The change in her life had been such a major one that even her metabolism was disturbed; for a few days she stayed on her boulder, or near it. There was little within her view to distract her except the campers; a number of birds that frequented the bowl in summer had already started to move down to lower altitudes, and because of the presence of people most animals avoided the place. She watched the campers going about their concerns or fishing on the lake, but the time was long for her.

The days dawned and crawled by; the campers moved about, the shadows lengthened and for a while there were lights in the trailers and waxing moonlight before the starry darkness fell again. She bore it all with stoical patience and didn't try to use her injured wing, as though she realized now that rest and immobility were necessary for it if she were ever going to use it again.

It was hunger, finally, that started her moving about once

more. Golden eagles, like their cousins the redtail hawks, can fast for surprisingly long periods and survive a time of hunger that would kill many other creatures, but Kira had never starved before and felt hunger more; besides, in the thin air of that elevation, the nights were cold and sharpened her appetite. At first she resisted its demands, but they made her increasingly restless; this restlessness aroused her nerves. They had been patterned for action, and their impulses had been suppressed for too long.

She couldn't go higher; the topography made it impossible and there was no prey for her where she was, or none that she could catch. Lower down she might stumble upon something that she could reach and hold; it would depend upon her luck. She picked her way down into the aspens again and turned along the slope to pass above the campers. It was her intention to get beyond them and drop down to follow the stream, in the thick growth there, for she knew there would be more life along the streambed.

She moved carefully, taking a few hops and pausing to make sure that there were no people in her path or anywhere nearby, for the memories of the man in the eyrie and the man who had ended her father's life from a distance lay like threatening shadows on her mind; these memories made her acutely aware of her vulnerability. She was so preoccupied with this awareness that she didn't realize she was moving more easily, that her injured wing didn't drag any more. It wasn't completely folded like the other, but it had come up; it was recovering. Her conscious control of it had become a habit from which some event, some quick emergency, would have to free her, but the time was not yet.

The two children that she suddenly came upon as she

hopped around a great boulder standing among the trees almost did it, but not quite. A ten-year-old boy and his sister, younger by a year, had wandered off a way from their parents' trailer, cleared a little space, and laid down branches around it; they were playing house, and had been so busy that they hadn't been talking. Kira stopped, startled, with her head up; then, recognizing them as enemies, lowered her head in an attitude of menace. Her eyes burned upon them and her crest stood out. The boy caught movement from the corner of his eye, and looked up. He scrambled to his feet and the little girl, following his glance, scrambled up too. They stood together for a moment, startled and indecisive, staring at the dark apparition that had so suddenly appeared before them.

For the children it was a moment more perilous than they would realize for a long time and perhaps never, for Kira had been put into a position of thinking herself cornered and was on the verge of attack; besides, she was very hungry. She had the strength and spirit to kill wolves and deer, and hunger intensifies these qualities; falconers who know eagles well and fly them are very careful with them when they are hungry. If she had never encountered men she might not have hesitated, but she had encountered them; the shadow they had laid on her mind held her still a moment longer.

The little girl broke the tense immobility that held them all; she screamed, and as she turned to run grasped her brother by the arm and pulled him after her. They ran screaming through the aspens and their mother ran out of the trailer to meet them. Fortunately for Kira, their father was out fishing on the lake.

After a long semicircular trip around the campers and the dam at the end of the lake, Kira came down to the stream. The bank she was on narrowed and grew rocky as the streambed curved into the precipitous side of the mountain and the canyon began. The other side was wider, with a longer, easier slope and thick with big aspens, almost junglelike with the close-growing trees, the undergrowth beneath them, and patches of sunlight. The road ran close to the stream on that side, winding to follow it, and after Kira had found a place to cross, hopping from one spray-wet rock to another, she was about to hop up the bank and cross the road when she heard the sound of an approaching car. It was an alien sound, and she stopped under the bank until the car and the trailer it pulled went past in a whirl of dust. The children she had faced and their parents were in the car; the children had been so frightened that their mother had insisted upon moving to another place. Kira's head was within the man's view, but he was so preoccupied by irritation at having to leave a fishing spot he liked by what he considered a bit of overheated childish imagination that he didn't see her.

She waited until silence fell again and crossed the road. Two feet from its edge she almost stepped upon a jumping mouse. Jumping mice are nocturnal, but this one was preparing to hibernate and was restless; it squeaked with fright, bounded across the road like a frog, and disappeared among the streamside rocks. Kira would have been glad to eat it, small as it was; the saliva ran into her mouth. She almost crossed the road again to look for it, but she had seen the people in the car and so associated the road with them and went deeper into cover. The place was quiet except for the

murmur of the stream; not many of the birds that nested in holes in the aspens were still about. The warbling vireos, which have the pleasant habit of singing while they incubate their eggs, were gone; only a red-naped sapsucker and several house wrens were still there, and they found Kira and scolded her a little and went about their concerns.

The morning's exercise had increased her appetite, and she was very hungry now; the roundness of her breast had fallen away and her keel was sharp, and the bloom was going off her feathers. The world beyond the canyon was full of prey that she couldn't reach and the small creatures about her, the least chipmunks and mice, were too wary and

quick-moving to catch. She tried to catch them. Reduced to bounding after anything that moved, she tried desperately to catch them and ended up panting and with an empty foot.

Toward the end of the afternoon a thin cloud moved into the canyon and leached out the light; there was a distant grumble of thunder. A shower was coming and Kira, well remembering what had happened to her once among the trees, found an opening higher up the slope with a group of rocks in the middle of it and hopped up high among them. The rain lashed her for a quarter of an hour and the shower moved on. She was left wet and on the edge of exhaustion by her hunger and the fruitless efforts of the day and sat hunched miserably among the rocks.

Close to twilight she caught a movement at the edge of the opening, and fixed upon it. It was a young bobcat, its brown fur and clouded spots blending into the rocks and the deadfall timber; lithe and easy moving, it looked like a bigger and more dangerous house cat with a stumpy tail and tufted ears. It turned its head toward Kira but its glowing eyes missed her; in the fading light her dark plumage blended too well with the dark, wet rocks.

It turned away to investigate the clutter of the deadfall, its stumpy tail twitching; its back was toward Kira. It was a dangerous antagonist, but Kira was beyond caution; maybe she recognized it as her last chance. She wanted it so terribly that the habit of favoring her injured wing was overborne; she spread both wings and launched herself from the rocks. From long disuse the wing was weak and almost brought her to disaster, but she compensated swiftly for it with her other wing and her tail and reached the cat; one foot clamped upon its head and the other upon its loin.

The cat shot upward like a strong spring released; its spitting screech shattered the silence. It threw itself and Kira about with blind desperation, flailing the twenty woeful knives that were its claws. They would have ripped Kira to bloody ribbons if they had found her, but she had caught the cat unaware and in the perfect position to hold them off; not all the cat's vitality and power could loosen her steely grip or enable it to turn and rake her, and presently it weakened and ceased its thrashing, and soon afterward was dead.

Chapter 5

FEW WILD CREATURES THAT sleep during the hours of darkness completely give up their awareness, and wake periodically to listen to the night. Kira did this on her rock and was more than ordinarily restless, for she didn't like being so close to the ground and its possible dangers; also, being in the air again, even for so short a flight, had excited her. Several times when she waked she stretched her wings over her back and exercised them as she once had when she was a nestling in the eyrie, to feel the life in them and the returning power. She was awake and waiting when the first glow of dawn stole into the sky, and as soon as she could see well enough launched out on a flight to another group of rocks across the clearing.

The wing didn't hurt her, but was weak; she felt that she

didn't have complete control over it. She was canted a little in her flight and automatically compensated for this with her tail; she reached the other rock and ran around on top of it in her excitement. She tried several more short flights, saw the remains of the bobcat, and dropped down to finish what she had left the night before.

When all the meat was gone she sat beside the picked bones for a time, quiet and content in the sun. She was still hungry and would be until her condition built up, but there was meat in her crop again and the urgency of starvation was gone. Her escape from death had been a narrow one, and she had been fortunate that her encounter with the cat had turned out so well; if it had not been momentarily pre-occupied with the deadfall timber, if it had seen or heard her as she sailed down from the rocks, she would have been lying beside it instead of sitting in the sun. Once committed, she would not have checked off it; they would have killed each other.

While she sat there a Steller's jay appeared out of the aspens, and seeing the bones checked its flight across the opening and dove into the tangle of fallen timber. It dodged about in cover, wanting to get a mouthful, scolding Kira; its dark blue plumage gleamed as it moved through the scattered patches of sunlight, and its crest stood up. Kira watched its antics until a car went by on the road below, reminding her that there were men about and putting an end to her satisfaction with the place. She decided to leave it; she hopped up the treetrunks to the top of the deadfall, and jumped into the air.

The wing carried her, and although there was still a feeling of weakness in it a fair breeze blowing up the canyon helped her to rise. The aspens, the stream, and the road winding along the side of it dropped away; she screamed with the pleasure of being in the air once more, of feeling the wind under her wings and being free of the earth. The fishermen on the lake heard her cry, and one of them who had been shot down over the flaming ruins of Dresden was moved to remember those days and wish that he could afford to keep a plane and fly over the quiet peaks that he had lived to come home to again.

Kira continued to rise as she went down the canyon, until she was high among the sentinel rocks that rose on each side from its walls near the crest. Her wing was tiring now, and she landed on a stony needle to rest for a while. Far below, as the canyon wound its way, she could see sections of the stream and its white water between the greenery of the banks; several miles down the canyon, on a point, a great rounded rock thrust out like a headland, smooth and eroded into a wrinkled pattern and golden brown in the sun. It was a wild and lonely-looking place, but the road was in it; it wasn't wild enough. Kira wanted emptier country, without the memories that this place held, and without the mark of man upon it. Not much that was good had happened to her in canyons, and she wanted to be free of them for a time. Now that she was whole again the urge to wander was stirring within her. The circumstances that had driven her from her home territory before she was ready to leave it were responsible for some of this feeling. If her life had been more normal she would still be flying about with her parents and hunting with them, but this pattern had been broken. The vast and lonely country beyond the canyon called to her but for the moment she would bide her time a little, for the wing would strengthen quickly with flying and while it did she would be safe among the high rocks.

A few mornings later, when the wind strengthened at sunrise, Kira launched herself and mounted upon it until the diminished lake, a glint of tarnished silver, lay beneath her like the head of a great serpent; its body was the canyon which twisted off to the east to be lost in shadows. Presently she was above the crest of the ridge and the country to the west opened up; the mountains descending, the wide, sweeping plain of the Wet Mountain Valley, and the great sawtoothed bulk of the Sangre de Cristo Range beyond holding the deep red glow that had moved the Spaniard Valverde in 1749 to liken its color in the dawn to the blood of Christ.

She straightened away beyond the ridge's shoulder, riding the wind northward above the darkness of pines, the long grassy meadows and shoulders, the pale gleam of barren rock. The early sunlight streamed through the notches and crept down the slopes as she went; the color faded to gray above timberline on the Sangre de Cristos, and the patches of winter's remaining snow shone white. The wing was strong now, and did its work; she was free of her long preoccupation with it and the boundaries enforced upon her body and her spirit. It could be that her spirit had suffered more, being a bold thing reduced for a time to caution, but the experience had been good for it. She had lived through the time and faced alone people in the shapes of children, and caught the cat that could have killed her. She was not so unseasoned as she had been before the limb had struck her; these things had helped her toward maturity.

The Wet Mountains along which Kira took her way were named for their heavy rainfall, and the lovely wide valley between her and the Sangre de Cristos was well watered and green, fine cattle country; toward the end of the morning she dropped lower into it to look for prey. A thousand feet below her a mink she didn't see flushed a family of mallards from a marshy creek, and as they rose she backed her wings and stooped at them. She flattened out behind them and slid up on them at great speed with the wind roaring past her. They saw her late and scattered wildly, shrill in their alarm, diving for the water again, but she picked out a young drake and followed him down; her foot closed on him. She bore him back to the mountainside, landed on top of a high, weathered pillar of rock, and ate him; a wandering sparrowhawk crying his "Killy! Killy! Killy!" took a few dashing stoops at her as the drake's plucked feathers drifted down the wind.

She watched a tiny golden-crowned kinglet flitting about in the spruces below her pillar for a little time, and when it vanished sat for an hour looking over the valley. Westcliffe and Silvercliff lay off to the north, little towns almost lost in the immensity of the green plain; beyond them the valley floor rolled higher and grew rougher again. Kira was coming now into country which echoed a rough departed glory, when men had swarmed into it eighty-five years gone to pan the creeks, erect their placers, or dig holes in the stony earth to search for gold. Somewhere beneath her as she traveled there would often be dim old trails or ghost towns, lonely cabins partially standing or weathered back into the earth, ruined stamping mills or smelters, old shafts that had produced wealth for a time and petered out or

never showed sufficient color and been deserted with a curse, or mines that were still worked. The most obscure corners of the high country had known the miners, as the most obscure creeks had known the beaver killers before them; between them they had opened the country.

The cattle, the ranches, and the roads that had followed them, the little towns to the north, were all within Kira's view and she didn't like them even though they were so widely scattered; the Sangre de Cristos across the valley, where clouds gathered around several of the fourteen-thousand-foot peaks, attracted her more. She dropped from her pillar and started for them, searching for thermals and soaring on them in the sunny silence toward the west. The ridge she had left and the greater one she was approaching

bounded her, but from her lofty pitch she could see them for many miles as they rose to their rugged crests, their shoulders and buttresses and canyons, the watercourses that creased their foothills and their timberlines where the dark pines fell away.

The peaks and their clouds drew closer, and presently Kira was above the beginning of a great boulder field beneath one of the gray summits; it stretched away in stony desolation, and she swung back over the shoulder again. A raven was flying below her, big and black above the last straggling line of wind-twisted pines; he cocked his head as she appeared between him and the sky, and dropped into a tree. She rolled over and stooped at him in play but instead of rising to mob her, as ravens sometimes do with eagles, the canny bird shifted easily to the other side of the tree and his bearded throat swelled as he croaked derisively after her.

She left him and dropped further down the mountainside, to where it flattened into meadows bordered with dense lodgepole and spruce. The grass had ended its growing and was drying to a golden brown, the few aspens showed their first gold; the afternoon sun had left the place and it was in shadow now, and all was touched with the thin, cool blue wash that comes to the high country at the onset of autumn. It was faintly melancholy in its beauty, which foreshadowed the winter soon to come.

Off in one corner of the largest meadow three cow elk and two calves of the previous spring were moving, followed by a bull. He was a splendid creature, standing five feet at the withers, with a sixteen-point rack that would have excited any hunter; measured along the beams it would have matched his height. The beginning of the mating season had swollen his neck and filled him with desire and fury; he stopped and filled his lungs, stretched his head forward, and roared out his defiance to any other bull within hearing. His bugling dropped to a screaming whistle, and died away in wrathful grunts; as Kira went over him he raised his head and showed her the whites of his eyes and dared her down.

She circled for another look at him, not having seen his like before; the cows and calves drew together and the bull bugled again. The voices of his ancestors had once stirred the wild echoes from Pennsylvania to Oregon, before they had been slaughtered almost to extinction for their meat or hides, or because they were big and made enticing targets, or even for their two canine teeth. They had been brought back in a measure; the hunting season would open on them presently, and they would face more trouble when winter drove them down to the farmers' haystacks.

Kira swung away from him and mounted up again, for the afternoon was ending and she wanted to be higher for the night. Presently she found a ledge that suited her and landed upon it. As the valley far below gradually darkened in the long twilight, a few widely scattered lights came on and, like distant stars, twinkled at her as she settled down to sleep.

Kira awoke with the dawn, but waited until there were rising currents to buoy her up. It was a clear and golden day, a day for wandering; her inclination was still for the north, and she turned that way when she finally jumped off the rock. She picked up altitude in long ellipses, and soon was above the high meadows and then the tundra below the peaks. In the fields of that bare and inhospitable world there were scattered alpine flowers and thickets of dwarf arctic willow branching low to the ground, occasional patches of snow in shadowed places, rockfalls and granite precipices; the air was marvelously clear, and cold and thin. White-breasted nuthatches, pipits, and brown-capped rosy finches liked it until winter drove them lower, and ptarmigan roamed its reaches; the little pica, the calling hare, gathered its grasses and dried them in the sun, packing the hay he made in crevices in the rocks.

In the distance Kira saw a roughlegged hawk suddenly appear from behind a pillar, swoop down a rockslide, and pick one of them up as he sat washing his face like a kitten atop a stone. The hawk landed and she turned to drift toward him, but he saw her and rose again and fled to cover in a jumble of boulders. She didn't feel like searching for him, and straightened away again; half an hour later she plummeted down upon an unsuspecting marmot as he lay stretched out near his burrow soaking up the sun. He was almost as heavy as she, fat and well-conditioned; after she had fed up well on him she found a little pond of snow water and bathed in it, and spent an hour drying her feathers and dressing them in the sunshine.

She was in no hurry to move very far now, and the bleak and lonely place suited her; she walked around a little, and finally jumped into the air again. Nearly a mile away a shoulder of the mountain ended in a lofty perpendicular rockface seamed and cracked by time and weather; there was a ledge near its crest, and she flew to it and landed there. She was out of the searching wind and the sun reflected from the rockface at her back warmed her; she composed herself to sit there for a while.

Beneath her ledge the gray granite wall plunged down to the rockslide below, which stretched about its foot like the frozen waves of a choppy sea; beyond it the tundra seemed barren of life. At first nothing moved within Kira's view, and she brooded over an apparently empty world. Presently, however, there were stirrings in the rockslide. The colony of picas that lived in tunnels in its crevices had seen her wide wings approach against the sky and, alerting each other with their squeaking, had retreated into their burrows. They were odd little creatures, distantly related to the rabbits but looking like big tailless mice. They loved their desolate world above timberline, and clung happily to it; not even the boreal winter that drove practically all other life to lower altitudes could move them out. One by one they began to move out of the darkness again to sun themselves before snow covered their haystacks and their entrances, squeaking to one another.

Kira watched them for a time, and then looked out over the tundra. The roughlegged hawk, having finished its meal, took to the air and drifted off. Long after it had gone a little family of ptarmigan, which had seen it rise and frozen motionless in a patch of dwarf willow, moved cautiously out on to the open ground and flew in the opposite direction. Their plumage was already changing for winter, and the sun glinted on a few white feathers as they went.

After they had vanished the afternoon wore on in quietness; Kira saw nothing move in the wide dun expanse within her view. Far off to the north a local thunderstorm piled up its clouds to shadow the mountains, and moved across the valley. The thin warmth went out of the sunlight as the sun sank down, and the breeze took on an added edge; the picas disappeared one by one into the rocks, still squeaking shrilly to each other underground. The high world, which has little that man wants, which does its best to discomfort and discourage him, prepared for its lonely night. Twilight deepened; the sky, which had turned a pale and luminous green, was leached of its color by the incoming tide of darkness with its freight of stars.

For the next few days Kira loitered along the Sangre de Cristos, soaring for hours when the mood was on her, sometimes dropping down to timberline or below it, sometimes looking down upon the peaks. She sat out several storms and saw several more from a distance, watching the dark coiling of their clouds and the lightning's fiery strokes, men like ants about their concerns, and wild creatures about their lives. Many of the birds that had spent the summer in the high cool forests were moving, or preparing to move, some to Mexico or South America or the Pacific coast, some down to the foothills or the prairie beyond the Front Range. Theirs was a vertical migration; they dropped down a few thousand feet instead of flying thousands of miles to the south. A few, like the white-breasted nuthatch, would spend the winter where they were, content with the loneliness and the heavy snow; Lapland longspurs and brilliant redpolls would come the curve of the world from Canada, and piñon jays would flock together and wander without apparent destination from timberline to the plains and back again; the shy hermit thrush, that loveliest of singers among the spruces around beaver dams, had already gone.

Kira saw many of them as flashes of color among the somber evergreens as she drifted northward; their presence enlivened her way. Once she stooped at a deadly little sharpshin as it chased a rosy pine grosbeak across an opening a little below timberline, although the pair of them wouldn't have made a mouthful for her. She did this in play rather than with serious intent, for with good feeding and freedom to move about as she wished she was coming into high condition again; the bloom was returning to her feathers and her bearing was more regal.

Snow began to dust the higher peaks, and dwarf oak-brush was turning crimson; cottonwoods in the canyons and aspens showed more gold. The forests seemed darker against this tide of bright color and lonelier as their summer visitors moved down; the vast distances of the land were often gauzy with morning mists and more enwrapped in solitude. Deer had come into their blue coats and would soon begin to feel the urge of the mating time; hunters were planning where to waylay them when the shooting season opened.

Moving northward through the early autumn as other birds were moving south, Kira finally reached the Arkansas, that far-wandering river which men had followed to reach the interior Rockies or branched away from near the mountains to move on to Oregon or Santa Fe. The mountain men, many long and dangerous miles from their base of supply, had used the river valley as a pathway among the peaks and opened up the country to the fur companies, the gold seekers, the emigrants, and settlers who had followed one another in their turn; the river had once been the northern boundary of the Spanish possessions in the New World.

Kira swung to follow it north, leaving the Sangre de Cristos at last. The Sawatch Range began, a new wall of peaks; a dozen of them, massive and gray and streaked with early snow, stood over fourteen thousand feet and bounded her to the west. For a time men held the stony valley, and she drifted above the foothills until the signs of men ran thinner and the river, with white water in it, was lonelier between the pines and the brown rocks. Beyond Buena Vista she saw a coyote on a sandbar in the river. He was old, and life had become a burden to him; he was hoping for a dead fish washed up, or some other flotsam to fill his belly. He was over a mile away, and she checked her long slide down the roaring air to take him in the loin with one great foot; when he whirled to slash at her, screaming, her other foot flashed out to close his jaws and crush his skull.

Later she went on again, and when Clear Creek came in from the west she turned up that narrow valley to leave the river for a while. The rising valley grew lonelier between its steep walls, the narrow road ended as a road among a few scattered, collapsing cabins of a ghost town that had been lively in the eighties and became a rutted track. One cabin was in fair condition, having been repaired, and a horse was grazing near it, the only sign of life in the melancholy little place; there were few trees, for it was close to timberline. On beyond it the valley opened into a great bowl ringed with the high, bare broken line of ridges between the serrated peaks. The lonely little group of cabins had been called Winfield, and there the gold seekers had given up; there was nothing beyond it.

Kira could see this from her pitch above the ghost town, and it suited her; there was no sign of man in all the great bowl within her wide view. The rolling earth was given up to sagebrush and alpine plants and loneliness; the stream wandered through it dotted with little beaver dams and lined with willows. She left the cabins behind and followed the stream for a time before turning off to the north to perch halfway up the ridge for the night.

The sun set and in the gathering darkness the granite walls on each side of her were washed for a little time with a fading, misty lavender light; the mountains across the valley seemed to move closer with the night. There was no point of light that Kira could see but around the corner of the ridge, in the only habitable cabin in the ghost town, the windows glowed. The man in the cabin was cooking trout for his supper, and talking to his big black tomcat. Kira hadn't seen him that day, but in the days to follow she would; he would be a trouble to her.

Chapter 6

THERE WAS FROST IN THE NIGHT; the early sun glittered upon it, and as it melted to droplets struck small transient rainbows from the sagebrush leaves. Kira, waking late, shook herself and relaxed her feathers again to let them dry. The morning was windless and it was too early for updrafts; she wasn't hungry and decided to stay where she was for a while.

In the cabin the man was finishing his morning chores. When they were done he took his coat off a nail and put it on. He did this awkwardly, for he was old and always a little stiff in the mornings. His hair was white, but he was thin and straight and his skin was surprisingly unwrinkled and clear. He lived with a daughter in San Francisco in the winter, but as soon as the snow was out of his way in the spring he returned to Winfield to work a little mine he had started five years before on a bench halfway up the western ridge. It was four miles from the cabin, and most of the time he rode the old horse to it. So far the mine hadn't produced more than a trace of color, which had soon pinched out, but he had great confidence in it. "No gold yet," he'd say, when questioned upon his return to San Francisco in the fall, "but the geology's right. I'll find it."

He picked up the cat and put it in an old knapsack, put the knapsack over his shoulder, and went out and tacked up the horse. The cat sat quietly in the knapsack, with only its head sticking out; it was accustomed to riding that way with the old man, and seemed to enjoy going with him. The old man did several slow knee-bends to loosen his legs, and got up on the horse. He let the reins swing, for the horse knew the way and was quiet; it walked down the rutted road for a few yards and turned off on the trail to the bench.

Toward the middle of the morning Kira cast up the fur she had eaten with the coyote's meat, and becoming restless jumped into the air. The bowl of the valley had warmed in the sun, and she found a thermal and circled upward within it. The valley dropped away as she followed the line of the creek until it swung to the south toward Huron Peak; then she turned northward away from it. Presently the land rose beneath her and she rose with it, borne up until she was above the bleak world of gray granite again, a roll of ridges and shoulders like a great frozen sea. Off in the distance, on a southern slope a little below timberline, she saw moving a band of creatures that were new to her and drifted toward them.

They were bighorns, those large, hardy wild sheep which moved about among the plunging cliffs and precipices of their range with consummate daring and sure-footedness. There were four ewes, three lambs born in June, and two yearlings fairly well bunched together moving across a rockfall to feed in an area of grass and alpine plants on the other side of it; two big rams with their heavy curling horns were on the top of a cliff several hundred feet above them. They had been bachelors together all summer and had just lately joined the rest; they were fat and in splendid condition from good feeding, and their brownish-gray coats had a faint purple sheen in the sun. Presently they would become rivals for the favors of the ewes and assail each other, backing off and charging together until an observer would think that their skulls would split and their brains would be addled forever. The crash of horn meeting horn would echo among the rocks; the contest would go on until one of them would stagger off defeated, and after the mating season was over they would be friends again. Being higher, they saw Kira first; they stopped and raised their heads to look at her.

As she cleared the top of the cliff three lambs below bouncing about in play stopped their gambols at once, instinctively knowing her for an ancient enemy, and ran to their mothers. The older sheep drew together; one of the rams jumped sideways out into the air and dropped to join them, coming down the sheer face of the cliff by jumps from one scarcely visible foothold to another. It was a beautiful performance, done with cool, split-second timing; the last drop was nearly thirty feet, and when the ram landed his belly almost touched the ground as his joints took up the shock like springs. He straightened up with a snort, and stood shaking his head at the eagle.

The flock was too closely gathered together for Kira to try conclusions with them even if she had been hungry enough, which she was not, but she landed on a high nearby splinter and stared back at the old ram. Her head was lowered, her dark hooded eyes were arrogant, and her golden hackle feathers stood out. She was telling him, in her way, that if she wished she could give him trouble; with his amber eyes on her he tossed the heavy, curling, umber-colored horns that would have been a trophy for any hunter and stamped a forefoot. She spread her wide wings and took to the air, but not to leave him yet; she wanted to play with him a little. She circled, hovered with slow wingbeats, and made several mocking shallow stoops; she raked off and returned twice more to hover and bedevil him before she tired of the game and went on. He had the last word by turning his pale rump-patch toward her as a roll in the ground hid him.

After she left the sheep Kira swung eastward, losing, for the first time, her intention for the north. There was a sort of indecision in her; the creek valley where she had spent the night still attracted her, and she wanted to stay near it or return. The wandering that a number of young birds do in their first year is, more than anything else, a search for a home territory of their own, and the creek valley, so wild and undisturbed, was to her liking. It is doubtful whether it would have supported her during the winter, for it was too high and the snow would be too deep; there would not in all probability be enough available prey in it, but experience hadn't taught her that yet. She liked it and didn't want to leave it, not knowing that if she tried to stay she would be driven out; her change of direction was in the nature of a preliminary exploration, a circumnavigation of the place, to know it better.

Except where the Arkansas River bounded it to the east the territory was enclosed by lofty peaks: Huron, Mount Oxford, Mount Bedford, Grizzly Mountain and La Plata Peak, all fourteen thousand feet high or higher, all of small use to man and little disturbed by him. She liked the sweep of it, the heights and valleys far below, the lonely magnificent distances with the color and feeling of autumn on them. She came over a big valley and dropped into it to see what it might hold to interest her; she wasn't hungry yet, but the skirmish with the old ram had stirred her blood and inclined her toward some other encounter. She saw several deer along the edges of meadows among the pines and then a scurry in a larger meadow, and swung over it. A weasel had been following a snowshoe rabbit, bounding after it like a small, implacable hound, and Kira saw him catch it when it tried to ram itself into a hole too small for it. She dropped to the ground nearby; the weasel, with his forepaws on his still twitching prey, raised his head on its snaky neck and turned his bloody face toward her. His eyes glowed with mad green fire, and he snarled at her. He wasn't over sixteen inches from the end of his nose to the black tip of his tail; he was turning white for winter, and there was no fear in him. In all the days of his murderous life he had never given way to anything, and he didn't intend to give way now. He snarled again, and bent down to the rabbit.

Kira didn't intend to give way either. She had decided that she wanted the rabbit, and the weasel too if he wouldn't leave it; she half opened her wings and jumped toward him. With a spitting snarl he launched himself at her throat like a striking snake, so swiftly and unexpectedly that Kira, whose strike was incredibly fast, struck late. Her great foot deflected him downward instead of closing on him, and his teeth met in her breast a little above her crop.

Kira recoiled with surprise and pain; she almost stood on her tail and rolled sideways, clawing at him with one

foot. He emitted a puff of stinking scent characteristic of any fighting weasel, and locked his jaws just before a talon caught him in the neck and opened him up. Kira jumped into the air and rolled about, continuing to claw at him, and although she soon reduced him to gory ribbons she couldn't break the hold of his jaws.

His muffled screaming and the tearing of his claws had ceased when her talon first caught him, and Kira grew calmer; soon she landed again and tried to dislodge his head with her beak. She bit through the remaining skin of his neck but couldn't reach higher, and finally had to accept the fact that she would have to leave his head where it was. For the first time she had run into trouble with intended prey; she had been careless and overconfident and had caught a Tartar, and the experience had been a lesson to her. She sat for a time in the meadow, looking about until her heartbeat returned to normal, and leaving the rabbit jumped into the air again.

The feathers about her breast were in disarray and bloody, and the inclination to bathe came upon her; she dropped further down into the valley to look for water. It was hard to find, but presently she came upon a small stream that started at an intermittent little spring, ran for a few hundred yards, and gradually dried up as it soaked into the ground; there was a good deal of water in it early in the year when the snow melted. There were willows around it, and aspen, golden now against the dark surrounding pines. It was a pleasant place and suited her purpose; she took a long, wet bath that cleaned her feathers and tried to get at the weasel's head again but still couldn't reach it. A few late-blooming plants had found their way to the bit of water and still clung to their blossoms in that sheltered place: blue harebell and the little red elephant, that delight of children, with its rows of tiny trunks and flapping ears, the spike of green gentian.

Kira dried herself and dressed her feathers among them and dozed a little; two deer coming to drink saw her and their snorts awoke her as they turned away. She stretched her neck to watch them as they disappeared, shook herself, and relaxed again; she didn't feel inclined to go just yet. The place was sheltered and quiet after the keen winds above timberline and fragrant with the scent of pines in the sun, an island of quietness in the clean and dreaming forest where time stood still for a little. Warmed by the sun and lulled by the silence Kira, indolent for once, drowsed again. Presently she was half-awakened by a sudden nearby scolding chatter and a rasping scramble of claws on bark; two Abert's squirrels almost ran over her feet, one chasing the other. She started wide awake, half-raising her wings and jumping a foot off the ground, then looked abashed when she saw what had roused her.

The noisy squirrels had shattered her mood along with the quiet, and her indolence was gone; she looked around the opening and jumped into the air and rose away from it, flapping heavily as eagles do when they raise their weight into the air. When she was a little higher above the pines the breeze up the slope caught and buoyed her and she mounted on it and turned southward; the afternoon had come and she wanted to get back to the creek valley again. Still higher she went, to cross the ridge on the other side of the valley, and could see the peaks beyond. Several of them bore cloud canopies and their sides were shadowed; there were other clouds gathering, for a storm was coming up. The horizon was darkening and thunderheads were building; one of them moved across the sun which sent long golden rays from behind it, and the more distant mountains took a chill purple on their slopes.

She came over the long shoulder of the ridge and crossed it, and the creek valley lay before her; presently she was above the old man's mine. Not far from it on the bench there was an old cabin, left from the mining days, which he had repaired a little to get into when storms caught him and he didn't want to sit them out in the dark little hole he had grubbed into the hillside. The cat was near it in the open, looking around for mice, and Kira saw it. She was hungrier now and wanted to feed before the storm; she half folded her wings and slid with gathering speed down a long incline toward it.

If the cat had not been surrounded by boulders she would have picked it up without slackening speed, but she had to check above it to drop; the roar of the air as she braked alerted the beast. It sprang into action without looking up, and streaked for the open door of the cabin. Kira still had a tremendous momentum; she rolled sideways, shortened sail, and swung after it. The cat fled through the door and Kira, three feet behind it, checked again and followed. Inside, she had to open her wings and take a backstroke or two to stop herself, and the backwash of air swung the door shut; the latch the old man had fashioned fell with a click. The terrified cat vanished through the one small window at the end of the room with a bound from the middle of the floor, and Kira was a prisoner.

The cabin was a single room, small and dark and bare, and after seeing the cat go through the window Kira turned to leave it as she had come in, but the entrance was no longer there. This confused her, and she stared at the closed door and the line of light under it. She moved a little closer to it; she lowered her head and her hackles rose as though threatening an enemy. There was no enemy; there was nothing but inanimate wood, shutting out the day.

Nothing like this had ever happened to her before, and she didn't understand it; she was walled in and the low roof seemed to press down on her head, which had never had anything over it but the infinite sky. She turned her head and looked up at it, crouched as though to jump against it, and straightened up again; then she walked around the walls and stood for a little under the window, but she knew she couldn't get through it and didn't try.

The old man had crawled out of his mine and straightened up as Kira began her stoop. He had seen some of it, staring as her great dark shape clove the air, hearing the roar of it; he saw the pursuit along the bench and the cat dive out the window. It galloped along the bench, between his legs, and into the mine.

One end of the cabin faced him, and he couldn't see that the door had closed. He stood for a short time waiting for the eagle to come out and fly off, but when it didn't he walked to the cabin and saw what had happened. He almost opened the door, and then changed his mind; instead he walked around to the window and looked in. It was rather gloomy inside, but enough light got through the window and the cracks in the walls for him to see the big dark bird in the middle of the floor.

Kira's eyes caught movement, and the old man's face appeared in the window; his pale eyes stared at her. She didn't retreat but faced him and stared back; her head sank lower and her hackles erected, a golden shower brightened by a ray of sunlight coming through a chink in the wall.

The old man had seen several eagles soaring in the distance; they were just birds, bigger than most but airy and innocent creatures, flying about. This one, a few feet away, amazed him with its air of defiance and power. The great hooked beak, the hooded unwinking eyes that threatened him, and the lowered head which was like that of a snake's about to strike sent a little chill up his back; he remembered its roaring, meteorlike stoop and its quickness of maneuver, astounding in a bird of its size, and was glad there was a wall between them. He continued to stare, fascinated, and no wild creature likes to be stared at; it is a gesture of hostility and often precedes attack, and Kira soon had enough of it. She began a shrill, high twittering that made him think she was going to jump at the window, and he backed away.

He stood for a long moment in thought, trying to make up his mind what to do. Ordinarily, he would have opened the door and turned a trapped bird loose, but Kira had become more than a bird to him. He was a contemplative man and there was little excitement in the life he lived, and Kira excited him; she was very different from the small, harmless and engaging creatures that he usually watched. She was one of the powerful ones who lived on the others, an aristocrat, fierce and deadly, the symbol chosen by conquerors; he remembered from his far school-days the Roman eagles and how the legions that marched under them had ruled the world.

Thinking of these things, bemused by them, he decided not to let her go. He wanted to keep her and look at her again and again, seeing the dark power that held dominion over the air. His desire wasn't like that of men who cage up strong beasts for the feeling of mastery that it gives them; it was more complicated than that; while he had her there he felt that his own life was richer because he partook of hers. But in the end it made little difference what his motive was, for the result was the same; he would keep her.

He looked around and noticed for the first time that a storm was coming up, and decided to try to get back to his cabin in the ghost town before it caught him. He went back to the mine and after some trouble got the cat to come out of it, put the cat in the knapsack, tacked up the horse, climbed up on it, and started down the trail.

Kira listened to the old man's footfalls die away, and then to the silence. It stretched out and there was nothing to disturb it; presently she relaxed her feathers and sat in gloomy disarray, occasionally looking about her. There was little enough to see; there was no furniture and nothing to break the monotony of the log walls except a small-ish fireplace at the end opposite the window with a rectangle of adzed logs, covered with a layer of gravel, set into the dirt floor in front of it. On one side of the rectangle, near the wall, there was a hole in the floor which had been made by a packrat that had built a nest in the chimney after the top of it had fallen in.

This bushy-tailed little animal was probably the richest packrat in the world, for in its trashy nest up in the chimney, out of sight, there were many gold nuggets. The two men who had built that cabin long ago had stumbled upon a rich vein studded with chunks of gold that started near the surface and constructed the cabin over it; the rectangle of logs and gravel was a trapdoor. The mine opening was only several feet larger than a man's body; it dropped down vertically for four feet and the mine angled off into the hillside, and there was a chamber beside the opening where the two miners had kept their gold in deerskin bags. In those wild days of claimjumpers, gunfights and stampedes at every rumor the miners' intention had been to store their treasure until they had a lot of it and then get it out all at one time; they had often argued about whether they would come back at all or wait for several years until the local population had been thinned by other rumors. Ironically enough, neither of them had profited; they had killed each other in a drunken quarrel one autumn night, and the trapdoor had kept their secret.

Long after Winfield had been deserted for richer workings and fallen into ruin the packrat had discovered the miners' legacy, gnawed into the bags, and after the manner of his kind had carried some of the chunks of gold to his nest in the chimney, replacing them with trash; others he carried to his alternate nest in a pine a quarter of a mile away. If there had been anything in the cabin he could have exchanged for the gold he would have done it, leaving a few chunks around for anybody to see, but there was nothing in the cabin to trade the chunks for; and the old man, like all the people who had been in and out of the cabin before him, had never asked himself why anyone would go to the trouble to build an apron before the fireplace.

As the overcast moved in and swallowed the sunshine it grew dim in the cabin; presently thunder began to grumble and roll between the mountains. The oncoming storm made Kira restless; she tightened her feathers and began to move about. She went to the window and jumped up to it, clinging with her talons and beating her wings, which were almost as wide as the room, but this got her nowhere; she couldn't have got through the window with her wings closed. She dropped back to the floor again and made several circuits of the room, but when the rain began she stopped in the middle of the floor and tightened her feathers to sit it out as she would have done under the open sky. The cabin grew dark, and thunder following the lightning flashes bellowed and shook the walls; the leaky roof streamed rain. The storm finally moved on and left night and drift of stars behind it, but Kira couldn't see them; later the packrat raised his head out of the hole, knew Kira was there, and withdrew his head again. In his cabin in the ghost town the old man blew out his lantern, pulled his blankets up to his chin, and in his mind's eye saw again his captive sliding down the air.

Chapter 7

WHEN DAYLIGHT CAME Kira sat, feathers slack, in the middle of the floor until a spider, warmed by the sun, began to build a web across the window. The spider was hurrying to catch a late fly or two before seeking a cranny for its winter sleep, and because it was the only moving thing within her view it had an almost hypnotic effect upon her. She canted her head one way and then the other and finally turned it almost upside down, for like most birds of prey she saw things above her in clearer detail from the bottoms of her retinas. She watched the spider until it was finished and grew still; then she moved to the window and stretched up to make it move again, but it was too high for her.

Now that there was nothing to engage her she relaxed

her feathers again and sat slack under the window. The wide sky and high places that she loved, the world without limit except the limit of her sight, had shrunk to the gloomy confines of the cabin, and she showed her dejection. A falcon would have maintained an air of contained alertness in her circumstance, but she was moodier than a falcon, and no bird shows its moods more than a golden eagle.

She sat on, rumpled and withdrawn, until in an hour or so the old man rode up the trail; she heard the horse, and grew alert. The old man, walking softly, peered in the window and she pulled her head in a little and stared back at him like a basilisk. She didn't have time to do more, for he didn't linger. He had a dead pocket gopher with him; the cat had waylaid it in the night and brought it in, and when he found it that morning an exciting idea had occurred to him. He went around to the cabin door, opened it a few inches, and holding the gopher at arm's length pushed himself partway into the room.

The click of the latch had turned Kira, and then the man confronted her. For all she knew he had her cornered and was about to attack; she would have preferred to avoid him but could not, and so she charged him. She didn't waste time with the shrill twittering he had heard before; her intention was not to warn but to kill him. One instant she was still; the next, with incredible quickness, she had jumped toward him and was halfway across the room, rising, her long legs reaching out, and her wings taking hard, quick beats that resounded in the cabin. The old man had a confused impression of a diabolic presence coming at him and terror hastened his reflexes; he managed to pull back, and had the door nearly closed when Kira crashed into the other side of it and slammed it against him, almost knocking him off his feet.

The old man stumbled backward and caught himself, then sat down. He had had a great fright; he was trembling violently, things blurred a little on his sight, and his heart was pounding. He had never been so shaken, and this frightened him too. There was a burst of shrill twittering from the cabin, which stopped almost as soon as he became aware of it, but the sound clung to his mind like the echo of a nightmare.

He sat listening with apprehension to the pounding of his heart, which had never concerned him before. But it didn't fail; it gradually slowed to its normal rhythm again and his vision cleared. He let out a long breath and shook his head, and realized that he had done an ill-considered and foolish thing: he had taken the first step in an effort to change a symbol of rapacious power out of a world different from his own into a docile satellite like the cat, and had almost been killed doing it.

He knew that he wouldn't make that mistake again, and wondered why he had ever thought of doing it; such a thing hadn't been in his mind at first. Then he realized that if either his captive or his heart had killed him the captive would probably be left in the cabin to starve, and he didn't want that. But it didn't occur to him, after the experience, to let her go; her headlong attack had made her a greater symbol than before.

He stood up on shaky legs, and deciding not to look at her again until later walked slowly back to the mine.

The old man had dropped the gopher in his haste to back out the door, and presently Kira grew calmer and ate it. It was little enough but all that she could get, and after it was swallowed she had nothing to do but sit disconsolately as the day went by. The old man looked in at the window again before he went home and left her to her prison and the night. During the hours of darkness the packrat grew bolder, and made a trip to his nest in the chimney. Kira was awakened from an uneasy sleep by the scratching of his claws, but after he made another noisy scurry or two she ignored him.

Dawn came again, and daylight; Kira cast up a small pellet of gopher hair under the window, and later the old man looked in. Kira gave him an unwinking and imperious stare, and didn't move. She wasn't afraid of him; her inherited reaction toward men was to avoid rather than to fear them. She had attacked him once and was ready to do it again, but she knew she couldn't get at him. He looked at her for a long moment and thrust a rabbit he had shot through the window. She jumped toward it with her hackles rising, and he turned away. He thought that she might start the twittering again if he stayed in view, and he didn't want to hear it; it rasped at his nerves and reminded him of his escape. Or so he told himself. What he refused to hear in it was an expression of willingness for mortal combat, if it would free her from her prison and the strange human whim that kept her in it.

Inside the cabin Kira hopped back into the middle of the room with the rabbit in her foot and sat holding it for a while, to see if she would be disturbed. The silence drew out and the old man didn't come back; finally she shook her feathers into place and bent down to eat. Golden shafts of sunlight falling through the chinks in the wall took steeper angles and finally vanished with the morning, not to return. She had had her little measure of the sun; the rise of the mountain behind the cabin blocked it out in the afternoon.

A week passed, golden halcyon days of Indian summer, clear skies and frost in the nights, the sun at midday blunting a little the keen edge of the thin, high-valley air. The packrat grew bolder still, and traded one of his nuggets for the cast pellet of gopher fur under the window where it couldn't be seen. The old man made his daily journey alone, for the cat had refused to come with him from the day Kira had almost caught it. He didn't miss it very much for his captive preoccupied him more and more, stirring his imagination, which had long been dormant, as the chewing of peyote stirs Indian medicine men to splendid visions beyond their daily reach.

Several times the old man caught Kira in an attitude of dejection and knew that he should let her go, but he quickly put this thought aside. His time with her was running out; they would be coming for him very soon, and the idea of parting from her began to disturb him. He had always slept like a baby after the exercise of the day, but now he often awoke in the night; finally he dreamed of sitting alone and idle during the winter in the clean, rather bare little room in his daughter's house in San Francisco and was so upset that his heart went into fibrillation. This was a new thing to him, and frightening; when the spasm had passed and he lay sweating in the dark he thought wildly of shooting Kira through the window and taking her corpse back with him to be mounted so he could keep her forever.

Finally, still thinking this, he fell into an exhausted sleep. A metallic crash awoke him; sunlight was streaming into the cabin, and when he went to the door he saw the truck and the horse trailer standing in front of the cabin and the driver walking toward him.

"Hi, old-timer," the driver said, grinning at him. "Moving day again."

The old man looked at him with dismay, and then forced himself to smile. "Morning, Luke," he said, and began to shake a little. He controlled the shaking as best he could, and added: "You're a little early this time, aren't you?"

"Same time as last year. Hard to say when it might begin to snow up here." He pushed his hat back. "Had your breakfast?"

"No," the old man said, and began to shake again. "I . . . Yes. Yes, I've had it."

"Good. We can start to pack up, then."

"Luke," the old man said. "Luke, I've got to go to the mine."

"Okay," Luke said, and grinned again. "If you've got to go. Need any help to bring all that gold down?"

"No. No, thank you." For a moment then he was his old self. "I haven't found any yet," he said, as he had said so many times before, "but I will. The geology's right." He smiled at Luke and was preoccupied again. "I'll be right back," he said. "I won't be long."

He went into the cabin and got the shotgun. He leaned it against the cabin while he tacked up the horse, put it in the boot, did his knee-bends, and mounted. Luke watched him, puzzled by the shotgun, but didn't say anything. As the horse ambled off he decided to write the daughter and tell her that he thought her father had got too shaky to come another year.

The old man was quite agitated when he reached the bench. He dismounted and tied the horse, started to take the gun out of the boot, and changed his mind. He stood looking at the cabin for a long moment, opening and closing his hands; he still didn't know what he was going to do. He was in such a state that he couldn't make up his mind, and put the decision off; he crawled into the mine, moved his tools further from the entrance, and sat down beside them for a time. Sitting in the darkness, he remembered his dream. "Yes," he said aloud. "Yes." He crawled out of the mine again, pulled the gun out of the boot, and walked to the cabin.

He stumbled when he was nearly there, and Kira heard him. She was sitting near the fireplace when he looked in, alert, with her feathers tight; a ray of sunshine coming through the wall fell on her golden crest and gleamed darkly. They stared at each other, the eagle held from the heights, tense as a strong coiled spring, watchful and arrogant; the trembling old man to whom she meant more life, who might yet take hers to hold what she had brought him. She lowered her head slightly and her hackles rose a little, gleaming; perhaps she divined, in some way of her own, what was in his mind and defied him.

Suddenly, in recollection, the old man saw again her swift and reckless stoop and heard the roar of the air through her feathers and was undone. He shook his head and ran around to the door, raised the latch, and pushed the door open with the muzzle of the gun. As it swung he ran to the corner of the cabin and stood there, holding the gun ready in

case she decided to attack him again when she came out.

Kira whirled as the door swung, ready for battle, but the man wasn't there. She jumped through the doorway into the bright sunshine and the world opened before her, the tall surrounding ridges and the sky. She looked at the old man, looked quickly all about, jumped into the air and slid down the slope of the mountain; as the old man watched her go his eyes filled with tears.

The narrow valley was below her again, the mountains rising on either side, the stream and the ghost town, the bowl beyond it surrounded by peaks. She swung toward it and found an updraft, and circled within it to rise. After the

dark confines of the cabin she wanted height and boundles freedom, and found them again; she was buoyed up unti she was as high as the summits of the surrounding peaks Around and beneath her was the crest of the Rockies, th longest mountain chain in the world, saw-toothed and con torted, with great seamed rockfaces standing out in ochei or gray, a great frozen granite sea, the peaks dusted with snow and the valleys and shoulders and high meadows falling down their sides dark with evergreen forests veined with brilliant autumn gold.

The vast sweep beneath her had once been the home of dinosaurs; through the crystalline air she could see the work of wind and water and ancient glaciers upon an ocean floor that had been uplifted millions of years ago and buckled by molten rock rising beneath and through it. She could see from the Continental Divide to the west, across the trough of the Arkansas River and the ridges beyond it to the east to the high plain of South Park, and turned that way. She was finished with the valley she had liked so well; once more a man had driven her out.

She was presently above Clear Creek Reservoir, and the river; a little flock of seven ducks passed beneath her. A long freight train a mile to the north on the tracks along the river had flushed them, and she dropped like a stone to pick one of them up. She ate it on a sandbar and bathed afterward, washing away the dry dust of her confinement, dried her feathers in the sun, and took to the air again.

There was high country between her and South Park; the Mosquito Range that divided Pike and San Isabel National Forests, and a scattering of peaks. She took an erratic course between them, and found the south fork of the South

Platte and followed it. South Park lay before her beyond Black Mountain, vast and gently rolling, over twelve hundred square miles of short grass and occasional long rounded hills, once a favorite wintering place of the mountain men nine thousand feet above the sea. On that high plain between the surrounding mountains they had found a better wintering place than could be found on the wind-whipped eastern prairies or in the closed-in mountain valleys, great herds of buffalo to live upon, shelter in the forests that lay about its perimeter, an immense sweep of open country and open sky.

There were several widely scattered ranches, a store or two along the road that ran like a ruled line for over twenty miles across the plain; some cattle, and on a far distant hill a small herd of buffalo that some rancher had put there, great dark beasts sadly reminiscent of the bygone herds that had found the country to their liking. Antero Reservoir lay a little to the south of her and she drifted over it; there were a few ducks on the water, and a pair of ravens were finishing one of them that had died of aspergillosis, a fungus that had killed its lungs and air sacs with filaments and choked out its life. The ravens halted their feast and cocked their heads to see what her intentions were, but she decided to ignore them; the duck she had taken on the river was sufficient for the time, and she didn't want theirs.

She drifted on, following the stream out of the reservoir until it joined the other fork of the South Platte. It ran quietly between its banks, into Eleven-Mile Reservoir a few miles further on; these two reservoirs and Cheesman Lake, around the end of the Tarryall Range to the northeast, are a part of the system that supplies Denver with water. She could see Eleven-Mile Reservoir from her pitch, but the mountains rose behind it and she didn't want mountains again just yet; she turned northward at the junction of the river's forks to stay over the plain, and held that direction until she came to Tarryall Creek where the mountains rose again and bounded South Park to the north.

Another eagle perched on a rock part way up the ridge saw her and took to the air; it flew toward her. As it came closer she saw that it was a tiercel, a young male of the year. They approached each other and circled, curious and not hostile. Kira gave her shrill, yelping bark: "Kee! Kee! Kee!" It was answered by the other bird and they circled higher, staying close together, growing accustomed to each other's presence. There was no reason for them to quarrel, no reason why either of them felt that it had to defend a territory. Mated mature birds engaged in the serious business of rearing a brood will hold a territory of their own and drive interlopers out, to assure themselves of sufficient prey, but these two were wanderers learning about their world; it would be several years before they would look for mates, and they felt friendly.

The tiercel, hatched in an eyrie in a canyon above Boulder, had stayed with his parents longer than Kira. He had been alone a shorter time and his wanderings had been uneventful; he was a little lonely, and pleased to find Kira. She was so much larger than he that at first he was rather cautious and prepared to sheer off but presently, assured by her voice and her demeanor, he rose above her and took a shallow stoop at her in play.

Kira took it well; she was ready for play herself; and so she fell in with his inclination. She side-slipped, recovered, and beating strongly rose above him and continued to rise. He followed her; being smaller, lighter, and somewhat more maneuverable, he threatened to get above her again and she began a stoop to unsettle him, banked away, and rose again. He raked off and rose with her; they drew closer together once more as they were borne up and the plain dropped away. They rose to a pitch beyond the reach of man's sight and cried their pleasure at one another and Kira, caught up in that pleasure, rolled over, backed her wings, and plunged several thousand feet down the roaring air to pitch up again and soar far below, waiting. Soon the tiercel followed her, tumbling end-over-end several times as he came the way older eagles do in their mating flights, a breathtaking and beautiful thing. He dropped past Kira and turned upward, scudding away from the earth in an acute and lovely curve; his momentum killed, he soared near her.

They were calm now, after their play; what doubts they had held of each other were gone, and there was nothing to vex their companionship. They soared out over the plain; presently they were above a pronghorn buck and two does, antelope-like creatures which are the swiftest runners on the continent. It is the only animal of its species in the world, combining some of the attributes of giraffes, goats, antelope and deer; once it was nearly as numerous in the west as the buffalo, but it had been woefully reduced in numbers because its meat was the tastiest of all four-footed game and its curiosity too great; now it is increasing again. The three pronghorns drew together as the eagles' shadows slid over them and the white hair of their rump-patches erected to flash a snowy danger signal as they do when the animal is uneasy or fearful, for eagles sometimes attack them or their fawns. But the eagles, not being under the exigency of great hunger, preferred smaller prey and went on.

They found it later in two white-tailed jackrabbit bucks that had fallen to fighting and forgotten their usual caution. They were leaping over each other in the open, each trying to rip up the other with the nails of its strong hind feet. They breed too fast and eagles help keep them under control; they are one of the eagle's favorite prey animals, and Kira rolled into a long-slanting stoop at them. The tiercel followed her. One of the jacks saw them and set off in great twenty-foot bounds across the plain; the other squatted. Either of the eagles could have picked him up but their attention was on the other and they swung after it, one on each side of its course. The jack was bracketed and couldn't take evasive leaps to either side; as they bore down on it the jack reached a bush and stopped under it. Kira stayed in the air while the tiercel landed and flushed the jack—the same tactic that had been used when Kira caught her first rabbit with her father—and again she caught it.

The tiercel ran to her and they ate the jack amicably together. When they were finished the tiercel's interest turned to the weasel's skull that was still hooked by the teeth to Kira's breast; he moved closer to her and cocked his head this way and that to inspect it. Finally he took a tentative peck at it. Kira bridled but allowed him; he took this for permission and cracked it with his beak. It fell off, and Kira was free of it.

Presently they jumped into the air and turned for the Tarryall Range, for the sun was dropping low and they wanted to settle themselves for the night. The tiercel led the way; he had been in the vicinity for several weeks, and had found a roosting place high in the range that suited him. There was a car moving along the dirt road that followed Tarryall Creek at the foot of the range, and as they flew over the road the car stopped and a man got out of it and watched them. He looked for eagles wherever he went, for he liked to shoot them and occasionally picked up a little extra money doing it. He didn't have a gun with him, for ground hunting wasn't his way; he found it more exciting to hunt them from a plane. From the white patches at the bases of their primaries and on their tails he knew they were immature, and judged they had wandered into South Park and would probably be in the vicinity for a while. He watched the direction of their flight until they were lost to his view, grinned, got back into the car, and drove off.

The eagles flew on, Kira following the tiercel to a bold, eroded, red rockface crowning the highest peak in the vicinity and overlooking South Park. The sun sank behind the Mosquito Range far to the west; its distant black line cut into the pale rosy sky. The tide of darkness deepened; in the twilight, when the world turns eerie for a little, suspended between daylight and dark and phantoms rise, the wide plain seemed to remember in lonely melancholy the great herds that had once moved across it unfenced and free, before they had been wantonly slaughtered for sport, or for their meat, their hides, or finally for their tongues, and the rest of them left for the wolves and the coyotes.

Chapter 8

ALTHOUGH GOLDEN EAGLES DO NOT usually mate until they are about four years old they seem to like companionship, and a pair of young birds that encounter each other and are compatible sometimes mature together and raise families until death parts them. This apparently was the way it was going to be with Kira and the tiercel, for they were pleased with each other. In the days that followed they were constant companions, hunting and roosting together, playing their Olympian games high in the air; they wandered widely over South Park and the mountains that surrounded it.

The sagebrush, a late bloomer, opened its blossoms, dusting the tops of the plants with tiny, sulphur-yellow flowers; ducks flying eastward to the Mississippi rested on the reservoirs after crossing the Continental Divide. The young ground squirrels, active longer than their elders, had gone into hibernation and the mating fever in the little herd of buffalo, which caused much roaring and fighting among the bulls, was finished and done. Mating time would not come to the pronghorns until a little later, but it had come to the deer in the forests bordering South Park; the bucks wandered about with swollen necks, ready for battle with one another and searching for does. The deer season opened and hunters were out after them; in this part of the state either sex could be shot.

As they moved about the eagles saw several parties of hunters below them; at this season men were likely to be in places that they didn't frequent at any other time of year. The tiercel wasn't much concerned with them, for they had neither threatened him nor interfered with his life; so far he had been unusually fortunate. Kira didn't share his naïveté. When she saw men moving in their jeeps or with a string of packhorses around difficult terrain, or camped among the evergreens with their campfire smoke rising like haze, she gave them a wide berth and went elsewhere. Her inclination to do this sometimes separated her from the tiercel for hours at a time, for he wouldn't always go off with her. After they had spent a day or a large portion of it apart their reunions would be playful and spectacular. They would meet among the clouds, soar together almost wingtip to wingtip, and finally hurl themselves down with folded wings for thousands of feet, sometimes corkscrewing as they dropped; or one, high in the air, would see the other resting on a rock near the top of a canyon at a great distance and drop roaring past into the chasm to swing up and land lightly a few feet away. When they did this they would, as like as not, stand close together for a time with their folded wings touching; they enjoyed an occasional slight contact with each other.

As the Falling-leaf Moon of the Indians waned the wind took the aspens' gold away and autumn turned toward winter; there were a few storms, the peaks gathered more snow, but most of the time the weather was good in South Park. One afternoon the small plane of the eagle hunter came over Wilkerson Pass and flew about for an hour, but Kira and the tiercel were hunting to the north in the Platte River Mountains that day and the man couldn't find them.

They returned to the rockface a little before sunset with full crops, for they had found a buck that had been shot and eluded the hunter to die in a little mountain meadow; it had fallen as they flew over it, and they had fed upon it.

Neither of them was hungry the next morning, but by early afternoon their appetites sharpened; they hunted for an hour without success, and then Kira remembered the buck. She circled to gain height for the long glide over the intervening ridges, and set off in its direction; presently the tiercel mounted up and followed her. They dropped after a spruce grouse in the valley of Rock Creek, but the grouse got into cover and eluded them, and they mounted again and went on. From their pitch they faced a gathering of snowy giants to the north: Torrey's Peak, Gray's Peak, Mount Bierstadt, and Mount Evans where the highest road in the nation winds into the sky, and turned east away from them.

They crossed the rise of the Kenoshas and Craig Creek and presently were above the dead buck, but a black bear was there before them; it had found the buck an hour earlier, and its belly was bulging with meat. The bear was in fine condition, fat and glossy; it had spent most of its time for the past few weeks eating around the clock to lay on fat against the time of hibernation and the fasting period just before it. It would go into its den with its belly and intestines empty, to be nourished by adipose tissue as it fell more deeply into torpor.

The dispossessed eagles circled over it, yelping their displeasure. If they had been starving they might have tried an attack, but the bear was a redoubtable antagonist and they weren't hungry enough to fight it. They dropped lower and finally Kira stooped, swinging up again thirty feet above the bear's head. It looked up and snarled at her, and as the tiercel followed Kira the bear sat up and swung a paw at him. Having got it stirred up they decided to make a game of bedeviling it; they made a series of alternate stoops from different directions, pulling out of them well beyond the victim's reach.

Several times, instead of stooping, Kira dropped with her legs thrust out straight beneath her, as though to take the bear in her talons, and rolled and slid away; the air roared with the swift turns and maneuvers of the two eagles. Although the bear didn't intend to leave the buck, or to turn his back on the eagles either, he didn't like the two great birds coming out of the sky at him; he got his back against a convenient rock and his head swiveled to and fro. He swung several times and then realized the uselessness of it; his snarls changed to a bawling protest.

The man who had shot the buck the day before had returned and was still looking for it; he was further up the slope in the evergreens and heard the uproar. He had heard the eagles' yelping but couldn't see them, and paid little attention until he heard the bear; he started for it immediately. Kira saw him when he reached the edge of the evergreen a hundred yards away, and giving an alarm call slid down the slope and away; the tiercel followed her.

The bear stepped away from the rock as the eagles fled, and the man shot him. He had been trying to get a bear for ten years, and was delighted with his luck. He was even more delighted when he walked up to it and found the remains of the buck as well, for it had an extraordinary rack and that was all that he had wanted in the first place. He didn't like venison.

A little snow fell on South Park but it didn't disturb the eagles or cause them to move; it wasn't deep enough to interfere with their hunting, they were already accustomed to it because they had often wandered over higher country where there had been snow for a time, and cold didn't bother them. Golden eagles are tough and enduring birds, amazing in their vitality; so long as there is prey about they make little of very inclement weather and extremely low temperatures.

This was a pleasant time for Kira; the companionship with the tiercel filled a need that had been left unsatisfied because of her father's death and her mother's somewhat premature hostility. There had been little play in the air with them for the sheer pleasure of it as there was with the tiercel; her wing injury and the confinement in the old cabin had rather knocked the spirit of play out of her, and coming to it now was good.

As they were in high condition and approved of each other there was an exuberance about them that neither would have had alone. They wandered more widely; sometimes

they played their games in the cold and boisterous winds around the peaks. The high country was emptier than it had been earlier, for many creatures had retreated from the snow and the increasing cold by moving lower, or gone underground like the picas which lived on their summer-gathered hay. There were still ptarmigan and snowshoe rabbits near timberline, but they were harder to find; the rabbits clung to the evergreens when they could, and the ptarmigan had moulted into their white winter plumage and took advantage of it by staying mostly on the snow. If they happened to move on to areas blown clear of snow they would spot the eagles a long way off and fly at their best speed back to the snow again.

Despite the more difficult hunting, however, the eagles managed well enough. Winter hadn't tightened its grip yet; the days were ever shorter, but the grim boreal cold that would presently lock the high country in a pure and frozen loneliness was still to come, and when it did they would drift away to better hunting grounds.

For the moment they were satisfied to stay where they were and sought the gales more often than not, riding them with shortened sail among the scoured granite peaks that sometimes smoked with long plumes of driven snow or hid their faces in the clouds. From the heights the long valleys and deep, shadowed canyons lay for miles beneath them; sunrises and sunsets dyed the mountain snow; and now, even more than in softer seasons, the two eagles in their freedom and strength and high spirits ruled the limitless and crystal-line air.

The day when it began was clear, with a fair wind; before the sun broke free the sky along the line of the eastern ridges was suffused for a short time with the color of blood. It faded before the tiercel awoke and shook himself, waking Kira; both birds mantled, stretching first one leg and wing together and then the other. They were not on their usual rockface but around a shoulder from it, where the wind wouldn't reach them in the night. Three deer far below moved back into cover, the last one pausing, with ears cocked, for a last look around before it disappeared. Nothing else moved, and Kira dropped off the ledge and spread her wings; the tiercel followed her.

They rounded the shoulder and caught the wind that was deflected upward by the cliffs there, letting it take them up.

This hour, when the rabbits which preferred to avoid the full light of day were moving back to cover, was one of the best for hunting, but the eagles had fed late the afternoon before and were in no hurry; they mounted higher, and turned for the Tarryalls. They separated over the higher slopes; there were several miles between them. A flock of ptarmigan on a bare saddle got up to move away from the tiercel, and, not noticing Kira, flew beneath her. She dropped on them and hit one with her closed foot. There was an explosion of white feathers; Kira swung up and dropped again, and picked the falling bird up before it reached the ground.

Instead of landing she mounted up again, and when she reached the tiercel's pitch drifted toward him. As she closed him she opened her foot, and dropped the ptarmigan. The tiercel waited a long moment as it fell, turning slowly and gleaming white in the sun; then he rolled, closed his wings, and plunged after it. He caught it far below, circled up, and dropped it in his turn. After Kira caught it she didn't rise again but flattened out, scudded across the slope, and landed on a high rock free of snow. The tiercel came down; above her he ended his stoop with a shift too quick for the eye to follow, and dropped beside her with his legs straight down and his feet open.

After Kira plucked the ptarmigan they shared it, cleaned their beaks on the stone, and took to the air again. They soared for an hour down the rise of the Tarryalls, moving in long, leisurely ellipses, leaning on the wind, pausing to circle several times above a herd of bighorns that had moved down a little from the peaks; presently they turned out over the plain. They crossed the road that ran to Fairplay, and near Antero Reservoir saw the three pronghorns again. The buck was restless, for the mating urge was on him; in his moving about he disturbed a rabbit that hopped a few feet.

Both eagles saw it at the same instant, and acted as though by agreement; the tiercel stooped, and Kira held her place. The rabbit ran back and crouched under one of the doe pronghorns as the tiercel dropped, and this confused him; he swung up again. The doe was frightened by the stoop, which came close to her; she froze momentarily in her fear and the other two ran in to her, for it was their instinct to bunch up for protection in such a case. Kira wanted the rabbit and as the tiercel rose up she stooped at the pronghorns in an attempt to frighten and disperse them; she came so close to the doe that one of her wings flailed it. The doe was unnerved by this and started off at full speed across the plain at the same time that the buck stood on his hind legs to strike at Kira; the second doe started after the first one, and then the buck jumped after them. The tiercel dropped down on the rabbit and picked it up.

The melee could swiftly have changed into an attack on the pronghorns, for eagles infrequently prey upon them, but it turned into a game instead. Kira saw the tiercel catch the rabbit; she had accomplished her purpose, and decided to chivvy the fleeing pronghorns. She swung after them; and the tiercel, with the rabbit in his foot, swung after her. They chased the pronghorns for half a mile, making shallow stoops above them, until they wearied of the game and came to earth.

A pickup truck moving along the road on the other side of the reservoir had stopped as the tiercel pulled out of his first stoop, and the man in the cab watched the affair. He was too far away to see the tiercel pick up the rabbit and he didn't see the end of the chase because the pronghorns and the eagles chasing them moved behind a hill and were lost to his view. He drove to Hartsel and went to the telephone in the store. "Jack?" he said, when his call was answered. "Jack, I'm at the Hartsel store. Get yourself up here. There are two damned eagles giving some antelopes a hard time near the reservoir, and they probably have one of them down by now. They ought to be around for a while and the weather's good up here. If you don't get those eagles there won't be an antelope around to shoot at next year. The eagles are worth a hundred apiece to me. Okay? Okay," he said. He hung up, bought a pack of cigarettes, and went out.

The two eagles shared the rabbit in a leisurely companionship, for the ptarmigan had taken the edge off their appetites; the sun was warm, they were out of the wind behind the hill, and they were in no hurry. After a time the tiercel got up and flew to the reservoir, to wade around in the shallows alongshore and drink a little; he had been going to take a bath, but decided not to. Kira watched him go, and while he amused himself in the water she jumped into the air and rose on the wind until she was high above him.

She circled lazily in the clear, cold silence, waiting for him, and saw him take to the air a little before the small plane came over Wilkerson Pass and headed for him. She had seen several small planes before from a distance; they were rather like large, alien birds to her, and not having a territory and eggs or young to protect she had ignored them. She watched the plane, not liking it but feeling no urge to drop toward it. She would wait where she was for the tiercel to join her.

The tiercel had risen to about the same altitude as the plane, and as he took a long ellipse it closed and followed him. There is partial federal protection on golden eagles and the pilot wanted the tiercel away from any road or habitation where someone might see and report what he intended to do; he wanted no complications. When he reached a point that he considered safe he swung to within forty yards of the unsuspecting tiercel and shot him. Kira had been too high for the man to notice, and he decided not to search for her; he wanted to get away, and banked the plane and went back the way he had come.

When the plane had approached the tiercel Kira had been of two minds; although it showed no evidence of hostility it appeared to be crowding him somewhat. The tiercel didn't seem concerned, but it made her uneasy; she thinned her wings and drew them in a little to let the wind hold her motionless. She was on the point of dropping down when the charge of number four shot smashed into the tiercel and broke him up, and she knew on the instant that he was dead; there was no mistaking that crumpling and the sprawling, lifeless way he began to fall. Some of the feathers were blown out of him, and floated in the air; to see him so violently transformed when the plane hadn't touched him confused and alarmed her, and as the plane banked away she banked in the opposite direction to get away from it. Her course took her westward, but as the plane grew smaller in the distance she swung back toward the Tarryalls and the ledge where she and the tiercel had so often roosted together.

Chapter 9

THE WHOLE GREAT SWEEP of South Park and the mountains around it had become shadowed with danger now and Kira's instinct was to get away, but her association with the ledge and the tiercel was too strong. She was drawn back; as the Tarryalls came closer she gained altitude again, and was very high when she came above the ledge. She made several wide circles and could see nothing in the vicinity that threatened her, and dropped lower and circled again before she landed on the ledge.

She walked about a little and then sat quiet and withdrawn, with her feathers slack. Above one of the distant ridges a dot appeared in the sky and she was betrayed by habit into straightening up to fix upon it, but it was only a roughlegged hawk on a hunting beat. It finally disappeared over the crest toward the east, and the afternoon wore on; later a few sleek Bohemian waxwings, down from Canada, moved through the pines below her. Shadows crept up the canyon wall and her urge grew stronger to be away before the night, but she sat on; the tiercel had become such a part of her life that her longing for him held her there. Clouds piled up in the west, and the sun dropped behind them leaving them for a time shot with fire and edged with rosy gold. The last thing she saw below her in the failing light was a great horned owl sliding across an opening, glimpsed and gone.

She awoke early, knowing that she was alone; sometime during the night the adjustment had been made. She would remember him for a time and often the wide sky would be lonely without his shape or his readiness for spirited play, but this would pass. Animals do not carry their grief for too long or dwell on the imminence of death; they are too engaged with living and handing life on. Had she been mated with him she might have held the territory and found another mate, but nothing held her now; she was free to wander again.

She dropped off the ledge, and around the shoulder faced into the blustery wind and rose on it; once more her course took her to the north, above the bony spine of the continent. In doing this she went against the tide, for most eagles that moved very far had already gone eastward toward the prairies or to the south where life was easier; she would cling to the high country for a time yet.

Her course took her eastward of Kenosha Pass, between Mount Bierstadt on one hand and Torrey's Peak on the other, both of them over fourteen thousand feet high, the

132

snow-tented pines and spruces stringing up the protected ravines, clawing their way a little beyond timberline. She was over mining country again where hundreds of millions of dollars' worth of gold, silver, copper, and lead had been taken out of the earth and a few of the mines were still worked; over ghost towns rotting or long since wiped out by fire or snowslides, old dumps, skeletons of mills, trails grown over, and the toil, hardships, rascalities, and passions of the thirty-year stampede for gold almost forgotten.

Georgetown lay to the east, one of the old mining towns that still had a drowsy life, unique in its quiet, nostalgic air of a New England or Midwestern village built into it by miners who, unlike most of the others, laid out a village green, put cupolas on their solid houses, and intended to stay.

She swung to cross the Continental Divide above the winding road through Berthoud Pass, the snowy lodgepole pines climbing the great slopes fitted as neatly together as the scales on a fish, and before the country descended again toward the long meadows and hills of Middle Park saw in the distance a moving white dot in an area blown clear of snow. It was a ptarmigan, and she knew there would be more of them on the snowfield nearby; she half folded her wings, and began her long stoop. Her speed increased; she was moving at better than a hundred miles an hour when she folded her wings completely and fell faster to burst among them as they flushed and pick one out of the air.

The wind grew more boisterous as she plucked and ate it, and an overcast moving in dulled the day; it swirled around her and thickened, isolating her from the world. It began to snow and the whirling flakes grew thicker, streaming out of the mist like a multitude of tiny silent ghosts.

Kira had encountered many high country storms which even in summer spit hail or snow and passed on, but this one promised more; she finished her meat, shook the snow off her feathers, and opened her wings. The wind lifted her up; the ground vanished from her sight; and she was aloft in a featureless limbo, but a map of the country she had seen around and below her was steady in her brain. She turned for the lower, more open country of Middle Park and crabbed across the wind, mending her drift, for she wanted to drop and find the limits of the storm before approaching the Divide again.

It made a great half-circle around her; she was now over the Rockies' western slope, which sends its rain and melted snow water to the Pacific. For a time she could see very little of it through the driving overcast; it appeared fragmentarily and was blotted out again. She held her way by wind direction and the map in her brain, dropping past the rocks of the descending ridges, literally feeling her way by the currents of the winds deflected from them; presently the overcast thinned and below its gauzy, shifting floor Middle Park and the valley of the Fraser River opened up. The storm's front angled back westward to the north of her, and gauging the speed of its approach she rode before it to a shoulder of the Vasquez Mountains that would shield her, picked a sheltered ledge, and came down.

The storm wailed most of the night, and blew itself out; morning dawned calm and clear. It was cold, and the great saucer that was Middle Park, walled in by a sea of peaks, lay beneath Kira in snowy purity, unmarked and still. Two ravens coasted down a ridge half a mile away, and in a spruce below Kira's ledge a white-breasted nuthatch gave its nasal "Yank! Yank!" but remained invisible. The crest of the great granite obelisk of Long's Peak, miles to the northeast in Rocky Mountain National Park, caught the sun first, and after it the lesser peaks; the sun cleared the Divide, and as the miles of blue shadows retreated glittered in fiery diamond points on the snow. After the ravens vanished nothing moved within Kira's view. Deer were yarded, mice and pocket gophers held to their tunnels under the snow, and beavers stayed warm in their lodges domed with white. Ice covered their world and was their sky, and the sticks they had gathered for their winter provender lay waterlogged on the mucky bottoms of their ponds close to the submerged entrances of their lodges.

As the morning sun mounted the sky Kira sat motionless on the ledge, her feathers slightly relaxed in the thin and pleasant warmth of the sunlight, and watched the still and silent world below. Although she was beginning to feel the stirring of appetite, she didn't want to move just yet; she had waked with a feeling of indecision within her. The inclination that had held her so long for the north, which had been in abeyance during her companionship with the tiercel and then returned again, was suddenly gone; not to feel the subtle urging of it, in effect like the urge that many other birds feel to migrate with the seasons, left her at a loss.

A few miles across Middle Park, which dropped to the line of the Fraser River, she could see a distant railroad and a highway where men and their machines were working to clear the snow; beyond this, between the Never Summer Mountains and the wall of the Divide, holding Lake Granby, Shadow Mountain Lake and Grand Lake, a great trough ran northward, holding the north branch of the Colorado River and gradually rising into high, tumbled country again. If her urge had still held she would have gone that way and for a time would have found prey that had come down from timberline into the lower elevation and the protected bowl that held the cluster of lakes, but now the urge was gone; she didn't know which way to go. In her indecision she grew restless and walked about on the ledge.

It was increasing appetite that finally got her into the air, and because she was at a loose end she followed the line of least resistance and set her course for the lower country of the lakes. She followed the Fraser for a little and swung away from it near Granby Mesa to come over Lake Granby, that long stretch of water backed and bounded by a rugged and sweeping line of peaks, but there was too much evidence of men beneath her; the highway along the lake, as well as the lakeshore itself, held enough cottages, campgrounds, and such to discomfit her and she wanted to avoid it all. She could have soared over these things and followed the Colorado River and the highway that rises to become Trail Ridge Road—the highest continuous highway in the nation—and comes out at Estes Park Village, but she did not. She found a thermal and begin to circle higher in it; the lakes and the bowl that held them dropped away.

The lakes are about eighty-three hundred feet above the sea; the peaks that wall them in to the east rise quickly to over ten thousand, and a few miles further east, at the Divide, thrust up to thirteen thousand feet or more. There were many peaks to the north and northeast of Kira as well; the park holds forty-two of them over twelve thousand feet high; and as she continued to rise the rugged panorama that opened up, with its summits and valleys, great snow-fields and canyons, gorges and precipices, seemed as vast as the world. Presently, high enough now for sight to clear the towering white wall of the Divide, she could see, through the crystalline winter air free of clouds for the moment, the distant plains and Pikes Peak fronting them far to the southeast. The plains seemed to hold more promise than the bristling, boreal world of the peaks, and she turned toward them.

There were flawed and bitter winds in the way of her going, summits blown bare and gray, plunging cliffs gleam-ing with ice, great gulfs of air beneath her, a frozen and arctic highland as empty of visible life as the moon. She crossed the Divide, gliding across a snowfield between two summits. Long's Peak, ruling all others, its granite obelisk three thousand feet above timberline, stood to the northeast of her; as the shoulders of the Divide dropped away into the bowl of Wild Basin with its forests and glacial lakes she dropped with them, past the first wind-twisted trees at timber-line, down into the spruces and massed lodgepole pines. If it had been a softer time of year there would have been a few people somewhere about, but they wouldn't have been a threat to her. No one disturbs the wildlife in the national parks; she was in sanctuary.

There was less snow here, for the wall of the Divide held it off; the lower altitude was kinder. As Kira came above one of the lakes a young doe was cutting across a bay on the ice. It was large game and would struggle strongly for its life, but Kira's hunger was urgent; she dropped upon it.

The national park into which Kira had found her way is

unparalleled in the long and spectacular system of the Rockies for the grandeur of its mountain scenery and the variety of its flora and wildlife. Both are protected from the enterprises of men, which so often destroy them, and because the elevation varies from several thousand feet above that of the plains to over fourteen thousand feet there is a great diversity; within that rise is found flora and fauna ranging from prairie to arctic tundra. The annual snowfall is about half that of the Alps, and timberline is nearly a mile higher. Over seven hundred species of flowering plants make the park a great flower garden as spring follows the melting snow of winter up the slopes until on the alpine moors miniature tundra plants only several inches high, diminished by wind and cold and pressed down by snow, many taking two years to ripen their seeds because of the brevity of their season, end the year's blossoming.

There was little life left on the heights near timberline now that didn't sleep the winter away in hibernation except ptarmigan and snowshoe rabbits; the deer and elk, the bobcats, bears, weasels, and coyotes which often wandered high in summer had all moved down, as Kira had finally done, into the timbered lower country where existence was easier. The basin held many of them and a rarer creature as well, one that has vanished from all but a small corner of the east and has now been hounded into the more remote corners of the west. Nearly every man's hand is against it; once it kept the deer from overpopulating their ranges, but men and their herds have increased, and sometimes it makes mistakes by finding men's stock too easy to kill.

Kira saw it materialize above her on the slope as she was finishing her meal, a tawny shadow among the pines. She had noticed a porcupine a moment before in that place as its dark shape moved slowly and erratically in and out of little patches of sunlight among the tree trunks. It was in no hurry; it never hurried, for with its armament of quills that held pain and often death for most creatures there was no need. Confident of its power, it didn't usually bother to stop when confronted by most of them but it stopped when the tawny shadow, the mountain lion, appeared in front of it.

The lion had seen it from further up the slope and moved closer; they both stopped and looked at each other with ten feet or so between them. The lion was a big male, a far wanderer, sleek, slabsided, heavily muscled in the forelegs and shoulders; the dark tip of his long, furry tail twitched as he considered the porcupine. Finally he took a step and stopped again in indecision. He was hungry, but not hungry enough for an indiscretion; his upper lip curled and he snarled at the porcupine, feeling frustrated.

After a long moment the porcupine began to move again; there was a tree nearby, and it waddled to it and began to climb. The lion took several steps toward it, snarled again, and moved off along the slope. The wind was in Kira's direction, or it might have scented the deer and investigated her.

The lion interested Kira; it was big, it had the air of a hunter, and it moved with lithe power. She stretched her neck to follow it as it moved off. It was soon out of her sight, and having a full crop now she took off heavily to look for it. Once under way she rose on the breeze, found a thermal and, not wanting to get too high because the shadows of the afternoon were lengthening, rode it up to the best altitude for observation.

Presently she picked up the lion again and followed its

course as it moved in and out of cover, winding about, often pausing on points of vantage to look around and test the air. Day was not its usual hunting time, but it had been disturbed that morning; laying up on a ledge above Thunder Lake, drowsing fitfully in the sun, it had seen a Ranger on patrol go past well below. The Ranger hadn't known it was there and it had got off the ledge, moved closer to him, and shadowed him out of curiosity for a time before continuing on.

From her pitch Kira saw the small band of elk lying in the little meadow lower down the slope before the lion scented them; presently she saw the lion's head come up and the stalk begin. The long tawny body sank lower and began to flow sinuously from one bit of cover to the next; each big

padded foot was placed slowly and with care, and the dark, restless tailtip twitched continuously as though to warn any other lion that might have picked up the scent and followed it that the stalker had the affair in control. Several times the lion was out of Kira's view where the pines were thick, and reappeared; it was drawing close now and slowed even more. Almost in position, it raised itself a little, with infinite patience, to look through the branches of a windfall tree. It could see the elk, picked out a yearling cow as its quarry, and decided to improve its approach; it backed with great care, inched a few yards to the left, and approached again like a stealthy shadow. Its back arched like a drawn bow, and each paw tested the footing to find it solid. A twig must have cracked, for Kira saw the elk bound up and the lion launch itself.

Its first splendid leap covered over twenty feet, to the top of a rock that the move had brought within its compass; from the added height the rock gave, it leaped again without pause and landed on the back of the cow as it turned to flee. The lion's jaws closed on the cow's neck, a forepaw caught the cow's nose and jerked its head back; the cow fell, dead of a broken neck and a severed spinal cord before the rest of the band was out of sight.

The lion crouched over its prey; it would eat its fill and cover the rest with brush and leaves until hunger brought it back to finish the rest, for it was not ordinarily wasteful. Having seen how one of the finest big-game hunters on the continent made its living, Kira swung away; the sun dropped below the crest of the Divide, the long shadows deepened in the basin, and it was time to perch for the night. She turned back toward the lake where she had killed the doe, drawn perhaps by the memory that there was still meat left upon it, and found a tall dead pine on a slope that gave her a wide view over the lake's expanse.

She settled down upon the topmost solid branch of the pine; the snowy wilderness about her faded into glimmering darkness. Presently the moon rose, full and golden, paling to silver as it mounted the sky, silvering in turn the shadowed basin; the peaks that surrounded it hung softened and insubstantial in the sky, gleaming mistily on their snowy slopes or gashed with black shadows. There were secret stirrings as the hunters and the hunted went their ways. A few hundred yards from Kira's tree a pair of spotted owls in a dense shoreside growth bespoke each other with hoots that sounded like the high-pitched barking of small dogs, moving a coyote further down the lake to sing a little in reply.

Kira awoke momentarily to hear it; its voice, more than any other the voice of the west, came in a series of short barks that increased in tempo and volume until it ended in a long squall, wild, ventriloquial, and eerie across the luminous night.

Chapter 10

A HEAVY OVERCAST HAD MOVED IN during the last half of the night and rested on the shoulders of the peaks; above it their crests stood bold and rugged islands rising from a sea on which the suffused colors of sunrise shifted and changed and spread. The peaks glowed with light and cast long black shadows as the sun cleared the overcast, which warmed and dropped like a receding tide and dissolved into scattered clouds.

As the ceiling wavered and broke, the half-light of the basin brightened and changed to day and found Kira still on the pine. She shook herself fully awake with a rattle of feathers, and looked about. In the distance she saw a gos-hawk suddenly dart out of the pines, swoop down at some quarry on the ground, and return empty-footed into the pines again; for some obscure reason the sight stirred a restlessness in her. The recollection of the prairies was still in her brain and their wide sweep attracted her; she didn't know that to go to them, to move out of the safety she had happened upon in the park, was to move once more into danger. Unlike the lion, which by good fortune had managed for several years to stay within the park and so keep its life, she was tempted to leave the sanctuary.

The lion had narrowly escaped being shot as a two-year-old when a hunter with two hounds had picked up its trail near the park boundary below St. Vrain Mountain and its glaciers. Before taking to a tree at the end of a two-day chase it had got into the park, and the hunter had caught the hounds leaping about the base of the tree, leashed them, and gone back the way he had come. He was a bitterly disappointed man to leave such fine quarry after the long chase, but he couldn't be sure that there wasn't a Ranger somewhere about and thought it better to be safe than sorry; after he had got well out of hearing the lion had dropped from the tree and wasted no time putting distance between them. This sent it deeper into the park, and so far it had stayed there; there was sufficient prey about so that it didn't have to extend its range.

For this reason it was in general safer and he was more likely to stay in sanctuary than Kira, whose range was greater. She had already traveled far and been exposed to more dangers, and would travel further and be exposed to more. Her inclination was for the prairies, flat and open, where prey during the hungry time of winter was easier to find; her inclination would take her away from the protected place where the lion would make out well enough

146

Too many men wished her ill, as they wished the lion ill, and in her wandering there would be more opportunity for them to work ill upon her.

The two of them were the rulers of their several worlds, marvelously fitted for their work, creatures of pride, beautiful in their vitality and power; a certain cachet attached to the killing of them for sport. Although their function was to keep their wild world in balance they sometimes killed men's animals when hunger and a lack of their natural prey drove them to do it. A few of them, in some circumstances and unable to differentiate, killed too many and drew down men's hostility on all; as men and men's works increased, their races were diminished.

Presently Kira remembered yesterday's deer, and dropped from the pine to go back to it. Other hungry creatures had found it in the night and there was not much left; she didn't go down but turned away from it, swung northeast, and gained height. When she reached her pitch she turned more toward the north near the park boundary, and moved parallel to it. Beneath her the land descended eastward toward the foothills and the plains; she was high enough to see the upward march of the world westward to timberline and beyond, the vast, cloud-shadowed sweep of the ranges she was leaving, Chasm Lake in its great gorge before the precipitous eastern face of Long's Peak, the work of ancient glaciers upon a land uplifted after the cooling of the climate ended the reign of the dinosaurs.

There was a highway near the boundary, and habitations increased; she drifted over Estes Park Village, and as the land rose again toward The Needles swung eastward once more for the foothills. The pines and spruces and aspen of higher country gave way to ponderosa pine, scrub oak and cottonwoods and brushy streambeds as the land flattened; lakes and reservoirs dotted the long, subsiding swells of the prairie, and farms, little villages, roads and ranches took over. It was too busy and populous, Loveland and Fort Collins and Greeley further east added to the clutter, and there were other cities to the south; Kira didn't turn toward it but held her course northward over the rise of the Front Range seeking a quieter place.

She dropped into the valley of Buckhorn Creek, seeing a rabbit there, but missed it; as she rose again, close to the rocky side, she passed at close range two boys who were playing Indian on a bench. They both had .22 caliber rifles; they had often watched eagles at a distance and longed for their feathers to make themselves war bonnets; suddenly having an eagle a few yards away, they acted with astonishing quickness and shot at it. One of them missed but the other was luckier; his bullet clipped off Kira's outer right tail feather two inches from her body.

As she saw them she banked away and probably preserved her life; she felt the bullet's shock and smote the air with her wings. Their attention was so engaged with the falling feather that they didn't shoot again but scrambled down over the rocks to retrieve it, and Kira rose away.

By the time she was above the juncture of the two forks of the Cache La Poudre River the prairie to the east had become emptier. There were no more cities, few small towns, and the ranches were fewer and more widely scattered. Beyond the two railroads running into Wyoming roads grew fewer and less traveled, the lakes and reservoirs supplying water to the cities of the south gave way to the dry winding beds of intermittent streams, and Kira saw windmills once again. The great plain, dusted with snow, stretched beyond her sight through Nebraska and Kansas to the Missouri, that wide river bounding a lost and greener world the mountain men had once remembered with a haunting song.

The shock of the mountainside ambuscade was still with Kira; the prairie was open to the sky, while the rocky, forested world she had known and loved so well now seemed full of secret places for foes to hide in and had almost betrayed her. She turned away from it, keeping a sharp lookout now for she was hungry; after the boys had shot at her she had given up any idea of hunting for a time. There were mag   her again occasionally, showy in their black and white coloration and a few flocks of horned larks rising and falling as they fed. It was afternoon now, a poor time for hunting, for any creature worth the effort of pursuit was in cover and would stay there if possible until nearly twilight; but far off she saw a redtail hawk circling and kept an eye on it. It was more familiar with prairie hunting than she, and might be useful.

The redtail finally dropped out of the sky and vanished into the brushy cover along one of the distant streambeds; it didn't come up again, and Kira drifted that way. The redtail had caught a rabbit, and if Kira had not marked it very accurately she would never have found it; it had hopped back into the thickest of the cover with its prey and crouched motionless, for it had seen her. The rabbit betrayed it, giving a last convulsive movement that shook the brush and caught Kira's eye as she hovered above it. She dropped into the dry streambed and pushed through the tangle; the overmatched redtail retreated into the open and flew off, protesting its ill fortune.

A northern shrike, down from Lake Athabaska for the winter, had seen Kira land; it flew to a high twig above her, turned its black mask in her direction, made a grating comment, and went away. She took the rabbit out into the open and ate it; the short winter afternoon was drawing toward its end by the time she had finished, and an overcast was moving in. The wind had picked up and there was a feeling of snow in the air, and Kira took off to seek a perch for the night. A few miles to the north she found a mesa that rose several hundred feet above the plain and a satisfactory rock on the lee side of it; the first snowflakes were on the wind when she settled herself.

The temperature dropped well below zero during the night; the storm lasted until noon the next day, and after it came a time of bitter winds, iron cold, and then more snow. Kira, staying away from the ranch houses and the stock near them, was hard put to it to find prey, and discovered what a prairie winter can be like. There was nothing to impede the northern winds in their sweep over the curve of the earth, and sudden, driving blizzards blotted out all sight; the hunted gave up moving about and the hunters went hungry. Kira lost weight and her keel grew sharp, but she was a good starver; otherwise she would have been dead before the weather broke. Many creatures died before a chinook, that warm wind from the west called "snow-eater" by the Blackfeet, came to ameliorate the distress of the living. It raised the temperature fifty degrees within an hour; by the next day brown patches of stubbled earth began to appear, and the evaporation of the snow exposed the bodies of those gone under.

As the snow diminished Kira learned, as all eagles do, to utilize the winter-killed animals for food when she came across them. She would have preferred live prey but for a time was too hungry to wait until she could find it; she was driven to build up her strength again as quickly as possible before the weather worsened and starvation threatened her once more. She was guided to this by another eagle that came into view nearly at the limit of her sight and circled down soon after. Drifting toward it as she had drifted toward the redtail when it came to earth, Kira found it in a fold of ground breaking into a young steer that had died in the storm. The other eagle watched her come down without hostility and resumed its feeding; there was enough for both of them. It was a young tiercel, and wore bells and jesses; it was her brother if she had only known it, escaped from the falconers who had taken it from the eyrie. It was very thin and in low condition, for it had had little experience in hunting for itself and had gone into the storm hungry. Finding the steer had saved its life, but only for a time; later it would drift south into Texas and be shot from an airplane, one of the many hundreds of wintering golden eagles killed annually in that state with the approval of the Game, Fish and Oyster Commission.

The two eagles took full crops together amicably and separated again. The tiercel went off to the east, to reach the border of Kansas before turning south to meet his fate; Kira dropped down toward the South Platte River and Prewitt Reservoir east of Fort Morgan. There was open water in the middle of the reservoir, with a few ducks and geese rafted on it; a bald eagle sat hunched on the bordering ice, patiently waiting for a duck to come out of the water and die. With the weather and the hunting better Kira left it to its chilly vigil and moved about. She didn't like particularly the flatter prairie south of the reservoir; several mornings later she picked a Canada goose out of an early flight, fed up on it, and drifted west along the South Platte to the five reservoirs scattered between Fort Morgan and Greeley.

She could probably have spent most of the winter in that vicinity, for the hunting was good enough, but there were railroads and busy highways and little villages sharing out the country between them and not to her taste. Deep within her the old inclination for the hills was strengthening again as the weather held fair, and the memory of the two boys had lost its sharpness because of this and the passage of time; all this bred a restlessness that inclined her to move again. She had already come a little way south; one morning she rose on the wind and turned that way once more. She might have angled across the foothills and the Front Range and followed them to New Mexico and the warmer lands beyond if fortune had not turned her back.

There was a farm where ringneck pheasants were raised in her path, and the long wire-covered pens were lively with birds. Such concentrations of game have a fatal attraction for hungry predators, and the farmer had erected a few poles with traps on their tops to catch the hawks and owls that were drawn there. They couldn't get through the wire at the pheasants, but the farmer liked to do away with them. There were two children playing close to the house nearby and Kira was too experienced by now to be tempted down from her pitch; but when she was a quarter of a mile away from the pens she saw a redtail hawk fly in and land on one of the poles. The trap caught it by the legs. It flapped desperately to escape but the jaws held it; it fell forward and hung head down and beat itself about, and the sight of its doomed struggles were so daunting to Kira that she swung a half-circle and went back the way she had come.

The next day, a few miles from the northern border of the state, Kira turned west toward the rise of the Front Range again. There was a gathering overcast and a keener edge to the wind, but despite the promise of worsening weather she felt more at home with the mountains near at hand and a lofty place with a high, wide view where she could perch at night. She had felt the coming change and fed well to prepare for it on the way; late that afternoon she caught a black-tailed jackrabbit that began to move about before twilight and fed again, then found a high, sheltered ledge a thousand feet above the plain.

The horizon drew in under the gray and darkening sky and nebulous shadows were swallowed by the night; well out the lights of a lonely ranch house twinkled like low stars. Kira remembered it, for she had flown over it after she ate the jack; the rancher ran several flocks of sheep, and they had been driven in closer to the barns because of the coming storm.

Kira waked for a moment when the first gust of the rising wind spoke in the pines below her, and again when the snow began. It was very cold at daybreak, and the wan world was blotted out by driving snow. The storm held all day and most of the following night; by the time the wind ceased its

crazed wailing and the last snowflake had settled down there was a foot of snow on the flat and great drifts had piled up about everything that stood above it. A stillness was everywhere and nothing moved. The hunted would stay in hiding for a time, avoiding the gleaming, traitorous world except in the darkest hours of the night; another hungry time for the hunters had come.

The rancher, who had lost two sheep to the coyotes in the last storm, had bought some strychnine and had been waiting for a time like this. The coyotes in their preying upon rabbits and other rodents had saved him in grass more than the value of several sheep; he had been told this but chose not to believe it. He had an old ewe that had been barren in the spring; he had killed it when the storm began and in-

serted a number of capsules filled with strychnine through its corpse. Before dawn on the morning after the storm he had carried it on horseback out on to the plain and left it there.

Being wakeful in the first half of the night because of the final violence of the storm, Kira didn't wake until the rim of the sun was above the horizon. A few thin clouds to the east had lost most of their early color but were still edged with rosy gold; it would be a long time before the prairie would show its first tender green and the tide of blossoms would flow up the mountain slopes, but the wide sky held a promise of the coming sky of spring. Kira shook herself and looked about. At first she saw nothing on the still, white plain, but as the sun mounted higher the shadow of the dead ewe stretched far across the snow. She fixed upon it, and as her fate decreed saw what cast the shadow: the final destructive gesture made by men against her life. These gestures had been many, but she had escaped them: the rifle that had killed her father, the hunter in the plane who had taken the life of the tiercel her good companion, the old man who had almost shot her in the cabin, the two boys playing Indian on the mountain bench. Probably she would not have escaped the strange ill-will of men for many years, for they were in an overwhelming majority arrayed against her, but at least she had learned to avoid them if she could; she had no defense against the poison waiting unseen and deadly to kill any creature that the iron necessity of winter brought to the carcass of the ewe. Being hungry from her long waiting through the storm she flew to it and ate.

With her crop full she sat quietly for a little and then got into the air again, for she was well fed now and it would be a splendid day for soaring, with the wind under her wings and vast distances within her view. She circled up, higher and higher, until she was a dot lost in the sky, and from her lofty pitch could see the mountains she loved so well rising ridge beyond ridge until they were lost in the distant haze.

But presently she began to sicken and her sickness grew worse; a convulsion seized and shook her, and as it ebbed left her with a heightened awareness of the world that had been hers, a lovely and unnatural clarity that held within itself a sharp and melancholy intimation of death. She knew that the crystalline air that had been her life, the medium of her comings and goings, her pleasures and her livelihood, was not for her now; she could no longer work her will upon it, it was her sudden enemy. The distances she had commanded and loved wavered on her sight and darkened, and she came erratically down. She landed badly near the snowy brush along a streambed, and staggered; the solid earth seemed to tremble and shift beneath her as fluid and unsubstantial as water.

She tried to face this trouble as she had faced many others, with her head high and her golden hackles up, but there was no enemy that she could face; it was within her. The second convulsion took her and muscular contractions began that she couldn't control, and she lost her balance and fell on her side. The contractions increased until they were storming through her in great waves, and finally her breathing ceased.

A junco, that happy gray sprite of winter, flew out of the snowy tangle along the streambed and was startled by the quiet, dark disarray of feathers on the snow; it turned quickly back into the tangle again. It would survive and greet the spring, and had no concern with the end of another's Odyssey.

AVON ◢ The Sign of Good Reading